The North American
BIRD
coloring book

Illustrations by Sally MacLarty
Text by David Hutley

First published in 2010 by New Holland Publishers
London Cape Town Sydney Auckland
www.newhollandpublishers.com

Garfield House, 86–88 Edgware Road, London W2 2EA, UK
80 McKenzie Street, Cape Town, 8001, South Africa
Unit 1, 66 Gibbes Street, Chatswood, NSW 2067, Australia
218 Lake Road, Northcote, Auckland, New Zealand

10 9 8 7 6 5 4 3 2 1

ISBN 978 1 84773 745 8

Although the publishers have made every effort to ensure that information contained in
this book was meticulously researched and correct at the time of going to press, they
accept no responsibility for any inaccuracies, loss, injury or inconvenience sustained by
any person using this book as reference.

Publisher: Simon Papps
Editor: Beth Lucas
Publishing Director: Rosemary Wilkinson
Layout: Sarah Williams
Production: Melanie Dowland
Based on a design by Janice Evans

Reproduction by Pica Digital PTE Ltd, Singapore
Printed and bound in India by Replika Press

Contents

Californian Quail
Callipepla californica

LENGTH: 10"

DESCRIPTION: A streamlined quail. Male has a protruding black feather just above a white supercilium topped by a darkish rufous crown. Throat is all black with a white vertical stripe separating a mottled neck; a dark eye and bill and pale forehead complete the head. Body is generally gray-brown with reddish flanks, a scaly breast and gray underwing. Female body much as male but head is brown-gray with black flecks and much smaller black crown feather; retains mottling on back of neck. Juvenile is generally brown and lacks crest feather.

VOICE: A haunting *ah-way-go* call is made to attract other quails. Emergency alarm call is *pit*.

BEHAVIOR: Spends most of its time foraging on the ground for food, never far from cover. Will burst into flight when startled.

HABITAT: Found in scrubby areas with dense cover nearby but will also move to more open farmland to search for food.

DISTRIBUTION: Found in good numbers on the Pacific coast from California to British Columbia and inland to Utah.

Northern Bobwhite
Colinus virginianus

LENGTH: 9.75"

DESCRIPTION: A small and quite dumpy quail. Male has a white throat and supercilium with a reddish-black crown (depending on race). A black band extends from the base of the bill, through the lower half of the eye and down to the top of the breast to encase the throat. Breast is white with black barring which merges into orangey flanks and undertail. Back is mottled brownish. Gray underwing is mostly seen in flight. Female similar to male but duller, with a buff throat and less obvious supercilium and black band.

VOICE: Seems to introduce itself with a *me-bob-white* call; also makes a whistling *hoy* contact call.

BEHAVIOR: More often heard than seen, spending most of its time hidden amongst vegetation as it feeds. Spends most of the year in fairly large groups known as coveys.

HABITAT: Farmland, grassland and scrubby open woodland.

DISTRIBUTION: Resident along the Gulf Coast in Mexico up to New Jersey on the Atlantic Coast and on an inland arc to Minnesota.

Wild Turkey
Meleagris gallopavo

LENGTH: 46"

DESCRIPTION: The largest game bird in America. Male has a glossy green-black body with a black chest plume and long pale legs. Primary and secondary feathers are barred brown and white; tail is large and fanned when displaying. Southern race has pale edge to tail compared to the eastern race, which has a much darker fawn edge. Head and neck are bare skin with a bluish crown and cheeks and pink-red neck wattles. Female and juvenile are smaller than the male, overall a much duller brown and often lack the chest plume.

VOICE: A loud *chack-chack*, and the easily identifiable bubbling *gobble*.

BEHAVIOR: A social bird, commonly found in large flocks wandering in search of food. Individuals have been known to attack people and even motorbikes and cars.

HABITAT: Woodland clearings, open scrub and occasionally suburban gardens.

DISTRIBUTION: Found in the east from New York south and cross country to Kansas with smaller populations toward the west coast.

9

Spruce Grouse
Falcipennis canadensis

LENGTH: 16"

DESCRIPTION: A mid-sized grouse. Male is dark overall with a mainly black head, a few white spots around the eye and throat and prominent red 'eyebrows'. The body is a mixture of blacks, browns and white, mainly barred to differing degrees with the breast being quite bold and the wings and back more defined; tail is short, mainly black with an light brown tip easily visible when fanned. Some races lack the brown tip and show white spots instead. Female lacks distinctive head pattern and is more brown with less obvious white markings, giving a more camouflaged appearance.

VOICE: Both male and female make a *cluck* call. The male also makes a series of low *hoots*.

BEHAVIOR: Generally feeds on the ground on fallen pine needles and berries. Can be quite confiding at times.

HABITAT: Prefers dense forests of pine or spruce.

DISTRIBUTION: Found in a swath across Canada from Quebec to the west coast of Alaska.

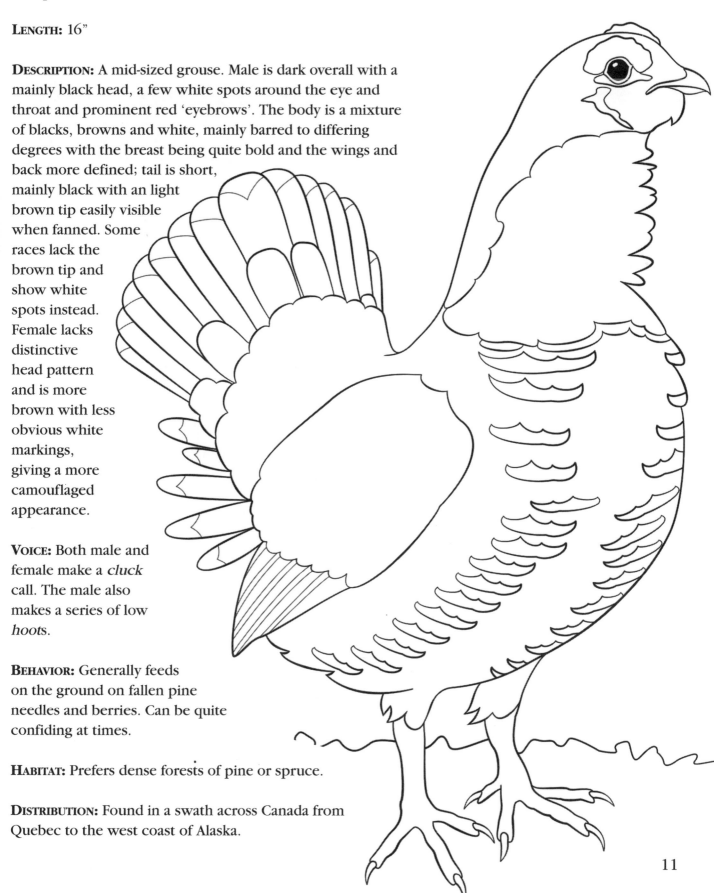

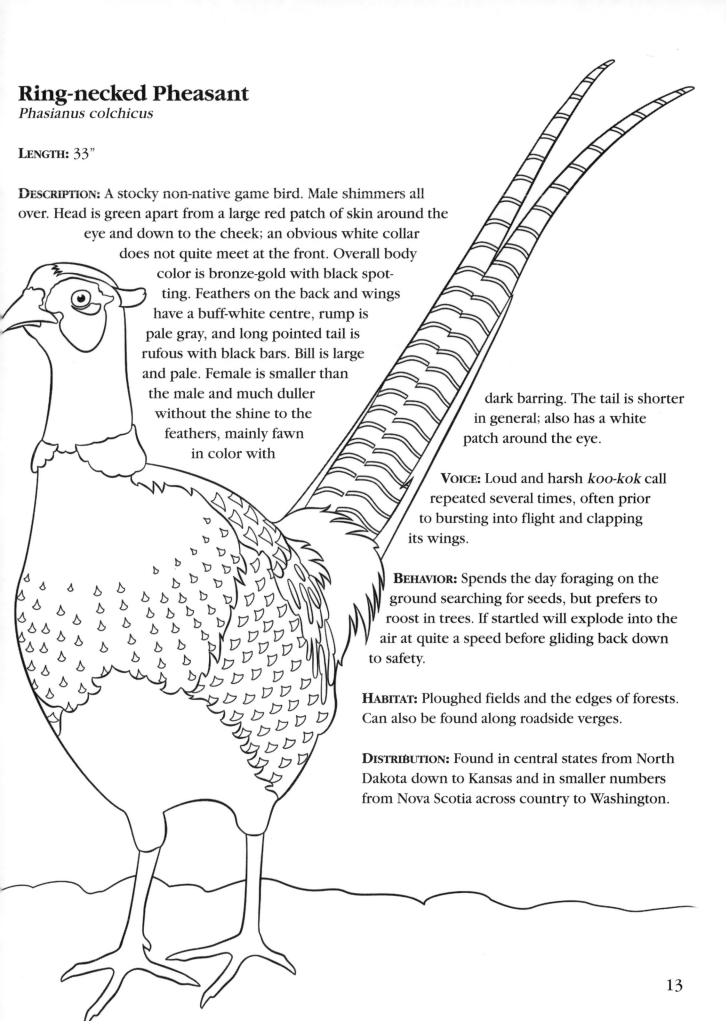

Ring-necked Pheasant
Phasianus colchicus

LENGTH: 33"

DESCRIPTION: A stocky non-native game bird. Male shimmers all over. Head is green apart from a large red patch of skin around the eye and down to the cheek; an obvious white collar does not quite meet at the front. Overall body color is bronze-gold with black spotting. Feathers on the back and wings have a buff-white centre, rump is pale gray, and long pointed tail is rufous with black bars. Bill is large and pale. Female is smaller than the male and much duller without the shine to the feathers, mainly fawn in color with dark barring. The tail is shorter in general; also has a white patch around the eye.

VOICE: Loud and harsh *koo-kok* call repeated several times, often prior to bursting into flight and clapping its wings.

BEHAVIOR: Spends the day foraging on the ground searching for seeds, but prefers to roost in trees. If startled will explode into the air at quite a speed before gliding back down to safety.

HABITAT: Ploughed fields and the edges of forests. Can also be found along roadside verges.

DISTRIBUTION: Found in central states from North Dakota down to Kansas and in smaller numbers from Nova Scotia across country to Washington.

Wood Duck

Aix sponsa

LENGTH: 18.5"

DESCRIPTION: A small duck. Male appears almost helmeted, with a small red, black and yellow bill and red eye. Cheeks are blue-black, a white throat patch curves to the back of the neck, crown is a vivid green and two white stripes almost form a V-shape pointing to a brown mantle. White-spotted purple breast, white underside, sides barred black and white and bluish flanks. Tail is black and legs yellow. Female lacks the garish head of the male but has a black eye surrounded by a fairly broad white eye patch; overall coloring is gray-brown with a mottled breast.

VOICE: Call is a harsh *oo-eek* usually made when disturbed and often while in flight.

BEHAVIOR: Generally likes to stay at the edges of ponds near over-hanging trees and vegetation. Feeds by dabbling at the surface of the water. Will usually form small groups but in winter can be found on more open water in larger flocks.

HABITAT: Small woodland ponds with good cover; more open lakes in winter.

DISTRIBUTION: Resident birds are found in two populations on the west and east coasts, with the larger one being on the east coast south to the Gulf of Mexico and inland toward the Great Lakes.

15

American Wigeon
Anas americana

LENGTH: 20"

DESCRIPTION: Male has a white central crown stripe that stands out against dark sides of the head. A dark eye is surrounded by a black eye patch flanked by areas of vivid green, the remainder of the head being mottled brown. The bill is a pale washed out blue with a black tip and black nasal spots. Body is a light brown-pink with a white flash on the side. Flanks are white in contrast to black undertail feathers; obvious white patches on the upper and lower wing are visible in flight. Female lacks bright colors, having an overall brown plumage with only a small white wing-bar; bill is gray. Juvenile is like female but lacks the white wing bar.

VOICE: A squeaky, high whistled *wi-wi-hew*.

BEHAVIOR: A grazing duck will spend most of its time moving around the edges of lakes and in marshes feeding on the short grass but is just as happy on the water taking food from the surface.

HABITAT: Marshland.

DISTRIBUTION: Birds can be found throughout the winter months around the coast from New York south to Mexico and up to British Columbia. During the summer months they move north into much of Canada.

17

Mallard

Anas platyrhynchos

LENGTH: 22"

DESCRIPTION: Largest dabbling duck. Male is striking with a shiny green head, yellow bill with a black tip, a white collar above a chocolate brown breast, pale gray sides and flanks and a light brown mantle. Upper and lower tail coverts are black but tail is white. In flight an obvious blue wing patch with white above and below is visible on both sexes as are the white underwing and orange legs. Female is mottled brown overall; head has subtle brown crown with paler sides and a black stripe through the eye which gives the impression of a supercilium.

VOICE: A drawn out *whack* sometimes repeated several times.

BEHAVIOR: Can be incredibly noisy and aggressive when in large flocks especially when fighting over bread thrown by the public. Usually found feeding on the surface of the water and regularly upturning so that its tail is pointing skywards.

HABITAT: Almost any expanse of open water.

DISTRIBUTION: Common through most of the United States and southern and western Canada.

Blue-winged Teal
Anas discors

LENGTH: 15.5"

DESCRIPTION: Male has a small round slate gray head with a large white crescent between its black eye and relatively long dark bill. Seen on the water the main body is brown with black spots, from the scapulars the back is black apart from an obvious white patch towards the rear. In flight, however, both sexes reveal large blue and white wing patches, green secondary feathers and orange-yellow legs. Female is mainly two-toned brown. The pale brown head lacks the white crescent, instead having a white eye ring and a white spot at the base of the bill that spreads down to the chin in varying degrees.

VOICE: A loud nasal *wehah-wehah*.

BEHAVIOR: Feeds in shallow water where it tirelessly swings its head back and forth while filtering water through its bill. When not feeding is usually holed up asleep in vegetation.

HABITAT: Marshland and shallow lakes.

DISTRIBUTION: Found from Alaska in the west to Texas in the south and up to Quebec in the east. Wintering birds are seen on the coast from Florida to Mexico.

Northern Shoveler
Anas clypeata

LENGTH: 20"

DESCRIPTION: Distinctive profile with long spatulate bill. White underwing coverts and green speculum bordered by white line. Male has black bill, yellow eye, glossy green head, red-brown flanks, brown back and black and white tail, with blue-gray upperwing coverts that show especially in flight. Female is speckled brown and buff, with an orange-and-gray bill, orange eye and gray upperwing coverts. Legs orange in both sexes.

VOICE: Male gives a nasal *chuk-chuk*, female a harsh *quack*.

BEHAVIOR: Feeds by swinging its broad, flattened bill from side to side in the water to sift out insects and plant matter. Usually seen in pairs in breeding season, but can form large flocks at other times of year.

HABITAT: Marshes and lakes.

DISTRIBUTION: Breeds northwest United States and western Canada. Winters along east and west coasts and in southern United States.

Hooded Merganser
Lophodytes cucullatus

LENGTH: 18"

DESCRIPTION: The smallest merganser. Male is unmistakable in breeding plumage with its jet black head, large white ear patches, yellow eye, and black bill. Breast is white with two black stripes at either side. Mantle is black and sides brown, with black and white tertials, dark and relatively long tail and orange legs. Female and juvenile have a chestnut crown, darker eye and pale brown cheeks and the bill is lighter to the sides and base. Breast is barred pale gray and the remainder of the bird is two-toned brown. The non-breeding male is similar to female but has a yellow eye and darker bill.

VOICE: During courtship the male gives a strange frog like burp-burp. More noise is made in flight by the constantly whistling wings.

BEHAVIOR: A tree-breeding bird. Spends much of its time on undisturbed lakes with plenty of overhanging branches to hide in. Feeds by diving.

HABITAT: Small woodland ponds and slow-running rivers. Will move to larger expanses of water during the winter months.

DISTRIBUTION: Winters in the southeastern United States from Virginia to Texas, moving north towards the Great Lakes during summer.

Red-breasted Merganser

Mergus serrator

LENGTH: 23"

DESCRIPTION: A slim sawbill. Male has a long orange bill, dark green head with a shaggy crest, a red eye, white collar, chestnut breast, pale sides and flanks, a dark back and orange legs. The female's bill is slightly shorter. Head is chestnut brown but retains a crest. Neck is pale with a gray-brown body, pale undertail covets and orange legs. Juvenile is like female but with shorter bill, smaller crest and overall duller appearance.

VOICE: Call is a rasping *hurh-hurh*, similar to the sound of sawing a thin piece of wood.

BEHAVIOR: Can often be found in large flocks, regularly diving beneath the water for quite long periods in search of food.

HABITAT: Large expanses of water and tidal lagoons.

DISTRIBUTION: Winters around most of the coast of the United States and can be found virtually all over North America during migration as it moves to its breeding grounds in Canada.

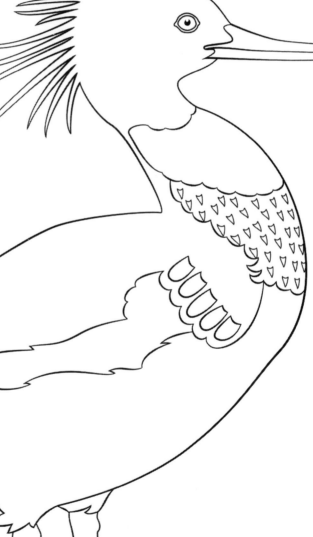

Ruddy Duck
Oxyura jamaicensis

LENGTH: 15"

DESCRIPTION: A small diving duck. Male has a large, pale blue bill, a black head and rear neck, two large white cheek patches, a rufous body, white undertail, dark legs and a stiff black tail, which often points straight up. Female has a black bill, dark crown, pale cheek patches with dark stripes, uniform dark back with paler sides, a white undertail and dark pointed tail.

VOICE: A series of *pop* calls that tail off into a *croak*.

BEHAVIOR: Forms large flocks on open water, where courtship displays are common. Males posture with their heads raised and their bill against their chests.

HABITAT: Open water and coastal lakes. Occasionally seen on the ocean.

DISTRIBUTION: Winters mainly on the east coast from Florida to Mexico although some are found on the west coast up to Oregon. In the summer months they can be found from Mexico to the North West Territories.

Common Loon

Gavia immer

LENGTH: 32"

DESCRIPTION: A large thickset loon. Sexes appear identical. In summer the chunky bill is black, with a steep forehead, black head with a red eye, and a black and white striped collar that is thinner at the front splits an otherwise black neck. Breast is pale and the rest of the body is black peppered with numerous white spots turning to squares across the back. The feet, seen in flight, are large and dark. Juveniles and winter adults are uniformly brown-gray with pale bill, throat and neck.

VOICE: An eerie call something between an owl's *hoot* and a turkey's *gobble* – some people say that it reminds them of whales calling to each other.

BEHAVIOR: Glides gracefully through the water, before all of a sudden diving. Comes into its element underwater, swimming from side to side looking for its next meal.

HABITAT: Large open lakes and coastal waters.

DISTRIBUTION: Found all around the coast of Canada and the United States in winter, moving inland during migration and throughout the breeding season.

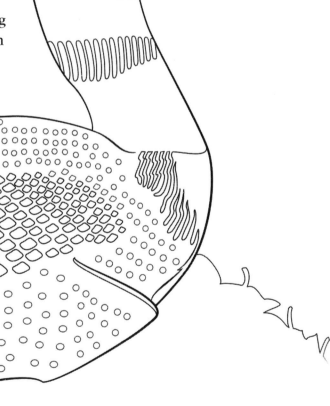

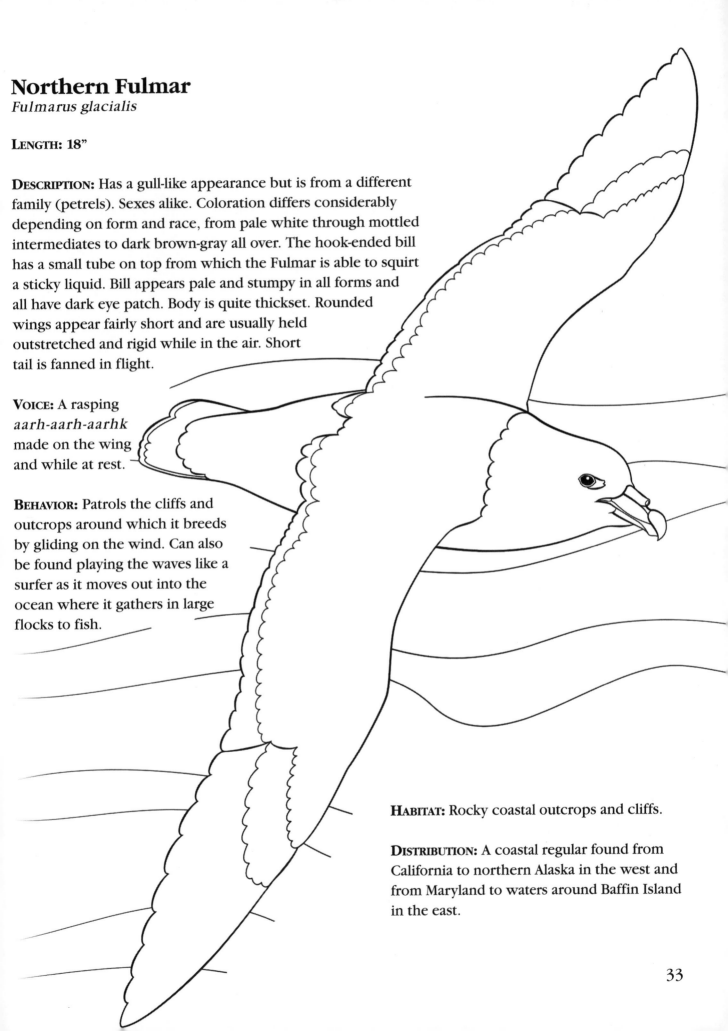

Northern Fulmar
Fulmarus glacialis

LENGTH: 18"

DESCRIPTION: Has a gull-like appearance but is from a different family (petrels). Sexes alike. Coloration differs considerably depending on form and race, from pale white through mottled intermediates to dark brown-gray all over. The hook-ended bill has a small tube on top from which the Fulmar is able to squirt a sticky liquid. Bill appears pale and stumpy in all forms and all have dark eye patch. Body is quite thickset. Rounded wings appear fairly short and are usually held outstretched and rigid while in the air. Short tail is fanned in flight.

VOICE: A rasping *aarh-aarh-aarhk* made on the wing and while at rest.

BEHAVIOR: Patrols the cliffs and outcrops around which it breeds by gliding on the wind. Can also be found playing the waves like a surfer as it moves out into the ocean where it gathers in large flocks to fish.

HABITAT: Rocky coastal outcrops and cliffs.

DISTRIBUTION: A coastal regular found from California to northern Alaska in the west and from Maryland to waters around Baffin Island in the east.

33

Pied-billed Grebe
Podilymbus podiceps

LENGTH: 13"

DESCRIPTION: Small grebe. Sexes alike. Breeding adult has a small but thick white bill with a black band around the middle. A black eye is surrounded by a white eye ring and a black throat patch comes down from the base of the bill. Head is two-toned brown with the flanks a warmer chestnut color; back is darker brown, undertail white. Legs are dark and trail the body in flight. Non-breeding birds lack the head pattern and juveniles have striped cheeks.

VOICE: Bubbling *gow gow goam* repeated over and over.

BEHAVIOR: Unlike some other grebes this one prefers to hide in the cover around the edges of ponds. Will feed on vegetation and small pond life.

HABITAT: Small quiet ponds, usually with protection from overhanging vegetation.

DISTRIBUTION: A fairly common resident in many states from Texas east to Virginia and north-west to British Columbia. Breeding birds spread north from this range as far as the Northwest Territories of Canada.

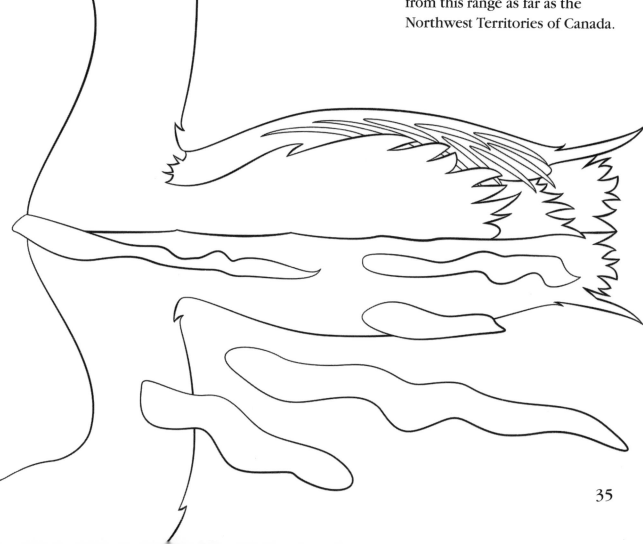

White-faced Ibis
Plegadis chihi

LENGTH: 23"

DESCRIPTION: A medium-sized wading bird. Breeding adult has long decurved gray bill. A red patch of skin from the

VOICE: A moaning nasal *urmn*.

BEHAVIOR: Roosts and breeds in colonies in trees, but spends the day in the shallows probing the mud with its long bill.

HABITAT: Shallow lakes, lagoons and tidal creeks.

DISTRIBUTION: Found mainly in the south from northern Mexico across the border and inland to Wyoming, west to California and east to Arkansas.

base of the bill to the red eye is surrounded by a white border. The head and main body are a deep bronze-red; wings and tail are iridescent green. Red legs are quite long and protrude past the end of tail while in flight. Non-breeding adult loses much of its glossy bronze color. Female tends to have shorter bill and legs. Juvenile resembles non-breeding adult with the head flecked with white.

American Bittern
Botaurus lentiginosus

LENGTH: 28"

DESCRIPTION: A large, slow, difficult-to-see wading bird. Sexes appear identical. Adult has a large pointed yellow bill with a black stripe leading from the lower base down past a white throat towards the neck, which is long when outstretched and has distinctive bold rufous stripes. The body is uniformly brown with dark centers to some of the feathers. Primaries are dark when you see them in flight compared to more pale secondaries, legs are greenish and long.

VOICE: Call is a *bloom-bloink* similar to the noise a stone makes when dropped in to water. Also a single *buk*.

BEHAVIOR: A secretive, skulking bird that spends much of the time hidden in marshy reeds, where it slowly stalks fish and frogs, sometimes at an incredibly low angle. More often heard than seen.

HABITAT: Large areas of reedy marshland.

DISTRIBUTION: Breeds through much of the central United States and north to Canada. Wintering populations are found south to Mexico.

39

Green Heron
Butorides virescens

LENGTH: 18"

DESCRIPTION: A small heron, even when holding its neck outstretched. Adult is a vibrant mix of crimsons and greens.

BEHAVIOR: A timid bird happier when under cover, it creeps through vegetation before crouching and staying motionless then bursting forward to grab small fish and insects.

HABITAT: Secluded ponds and rivers with plenty of cover.

DISTRIBUTION: Found in the east from New Hampshire inland to South Dakota and south to Mexico. Smaller numbers are also found along the west cost to Oregon.

Bill is quite long, dark above and yellow below. A yellow flash is in front of the eye, which is also yellow. The crown is black and the sides of the head and the neck are dark crimson. White streaks down the front, wings and back are a shiny green, underparts are light gray and legs are orange. Juvenile is duller than the adult, having a mottled brown streaked neck and greenish legs.

VOICE: A high *skeek* repeated over and over.

41

Cattle Egret
Bubulcus ibis

LENGTH: 20"

DESCRIPTION: A small and colorful, thickset egret. Breeding adult has a robust bill, yellow at the tip turning more orange-red towards the base. Eye is red, main body is white with gingery buff patches on breast, back and crown, which is slightly raised to a crest. Legs are pinkish red. Winter-juvenile lacks buff coloration; bill and eye are yellow and legs dark.

VOICE: Fairly quiet when not breeding, giving only the occasional *krek* call. When in colonies more vocal with a *quack* like a toy duck.

BEHAVIOR: A social bird often found in flocks. As the name suggests, Cattle Egrets are commonly found close to livestock, which they follow around feeding on insects; can sometimes be seen catching a ride on the back of larger animals.

HABITAT: Found in marshland and dry grassland near to livestock.

DISTRIBUTION: Fairly common along the south coast from Florida, across the border to Mexico and inland to Colorado.

Great Blue Heron

Ardea herodias

LENGTH: 46"

DESCRIPTION: North America's largest heron. Adult has a large, heavy, pointed yellow bill, black lores and a yellow eye. The head has a white crown stripe flanked by two black stripes starting just behind the eye that form two plumes. White cheeks and throat merge in to a brown-gray neck with black and white stripes at the front. Main body and tail are pale slate gray with back and chest plumes; legs are long and dusky. In flight visible primaries and secondaries are black. Each wing has pale spots at the shoulder. Juvenile much grayer overall with a black crown.

VOICE: Can be vocal, especially in flight, giving a deep *craak* call. Also makes a lower *fraenk* call.

BEHAVIOR: Usually seen quietly fishing in shallow water. Moving slowly it stalks its prey before plunging its long bill into the water to catch its target. Nests in trees in large groups.

DISTRIBUTION: Common throughout the United States and as far north as the tip of Alberta.

45

Brown Pelican
Pelecanus occidentalis

LENGTH: 51"

DESCRIPTION: The unmistakable breeding adult has a large multi-colored bill with a mixture of orangey-red, black and pale yellow above and black below and a large pouch. In some birds the colors are much brighter and the pouch red. Head is yellow with a white stripe from the base of the bill down the throat to the front of the breast. The rest of the neck is chestnut brown with a yellow patch at the top of the breast. Underside is dark brown, back and tail are light gray. Legs are short and black with webbed feet. Non-breeding birds are less colorful, being whiter overall. Juvenile has a gray bill, brown head, neck and body and underside.

VOICE: Mostly silent except when in the nest. The young make a series of *squeek* noises.

BEHAVIOR: Often seen on the water or sitting on piers and breakwaters, these acrobatic birds circle in the sky before twisting and plunging into the ocean to catch fish in their massive pouch.

HABITAT: Coastal waters.

DISTRIBUTION: Rarely seen inland. Found in the east from North Carolina to Texas and on the west coast around California.

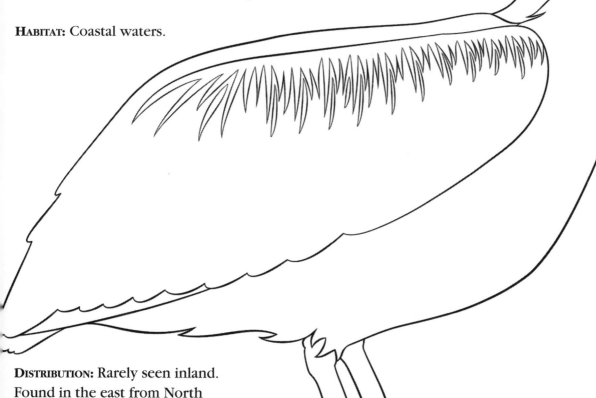

Double-crested Cormorant
Phalacrocorax auritus

LENGTH: 33"

DESCRIPTION: Male and female look identical. Adult breeding birds appear black with yellow throat patches, but on closer inspection the wings are dark iridescent green. Head has two tufts of feathers extending from the back of the crown ranging from black and hard to see to white and obvious depending on the race. Eyes are green and tail is quite long. When in flight a kink to the neck is visible. Non-breeding birds lack the tufts. Juvenile birds are generally light brown with pale chest and underparts. All forms retain the yellow throat patch.

VOICE: A deep throaty *croak* is made by the adults around the nest site. Young birds make a high pitched *yea-yea* call.

BEHAVIOR: Will feed happily both in the ocean and inland on large lakes, where it swims across the water before diving below the surface to take fish. After diving all cormorants perch and stretch out the wings to dry.

HABITAT: Open ocean, coastal bays and inland lakes.

DISTRIBUTION: These birds can turn up almost anywhere in the United States during migration but prefer to spend the winter on the southern coast from Florida to Mexico.

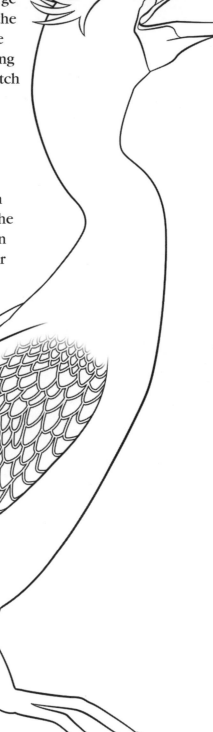

Turkey Vulture
Cathartes aura

LENGTH: 26"

DESCRIPTION: Adult has a hooked white bill that stands out against a featherless red head and dark eye. When perched overall body and tail color appears brown; in flight contrasting paler primary and secondary feathers can be seen. Legs are pale. Juveniles have a brownish-pink head that brightens with age.

VOICE: Once fledged, usually silent. Nestlings give off a rasping *hiss.*

BEHAVIOR: Like most vultures they are often seen circling overhead looking for carrion. Once their excellent sense of smell locates a meal they will gather in sometimes large numbers to feed and will push their featherless head deep inside the carcass to find soft meat to eat. Roost in large flocks, usually in trees.

HABITAT: Open grassland and farmland.

DISTRIBUTION: Found year-round from Virginia to California. Breeding birds are also found inland across the United States and in southern Canada.

51

American Kestrel
Falco sparverius

LENGTH: 9"

DESCRIPTION: A small falcon. Male has small dark hooked beak with yellow nostril patch. Eye is dark, head is mainly light gray and white apart from a rufous "thumb print" on the crown. Two black lines can be seen below and behind the eye. Many of the feathers on the body have black centers. Breast and underside are pale buff, back and tail are rufous with a black tip to the tail, wings are light blue-gray with black primaries and the feet are yellow. Female has lighter gray and white head pattern and is mainly rufous with black barring rather than spots.

VOICE: A repetitive series of high pitched *kiy-kiy-kiy* notes.

BEHAVIOR: Hunting bird will fly up from its perch, which could be a road sign, telephone wire or tree, soar into the sky then fan out its tail and hover in midair before dropping down to its target.

HABITAT: Parks, open grassland and cities.

DISTRIBUTION: Resident across much of the United States with summering birds found further north from North Dakota up into Alaska.

53

VOICE: A surprisingly weak series of whistles.

BEHAVIOR: Mostly seen by water, their main diet is fish although they will catch wildfowl and also feed on carrion. Will form large flocks if food is in good supply.

HABITAT: Rivers, lakes and coastal waters.

DISTRIBUTION: Found on the west coast from northern California to Alaska with summering birds seen throughout much of Canada. Wintering numbers increase inland through Montana south to Texas.

Bald Eagle
Haliaeetus leucocephalus

LENGTH: 31"

DESCRIPTION: This symbol of the United States is not, as its name suggests, bald. In fact the adult has a full head of bright white feathers flanking a huge hooked yellow bill and orangey-yellow eye. The tail is also bright white and the remainder of the bird is a rich chocolate brown, including the feathering down the legs to its bright yellow feet. Juveniles take around four years to reach adulthood, during which time they change from generally all brown to gain some white markings on the body and head. Near-adults show a brown eye-stripe and dirty yellow beak. Feet remain yellow in all ages.

Cooper's Hawk

Accipiter cooperii

LENGTH:
16.5"

DESCRIPTION: A mid-sized hawk. Adult has small, sharp, hooked, yellow and gray beak; a white patch at the base highlights the orange eye. Cheeks are pale with a hint of orange buffing, throat is pale, breast barred orange and white, vent area white. The crown down to the back of the neck is black and wings are slate gray, as is the tail, which is barred black with a white tip. Legs are yellow. The female is larger and sometimes a little darker. Juvenile's head and nape are mottled orange-black, the back is browner overall and from the throat down is pale buff-white with black streaking.

VOICE: A high-pitched series of *kak-kak-kak* alarm calls is most often heard, although females will make high whistles when calling for food from the male when young are in the nest.

BEHAVIOR: Hunts mainly small birds and mammals and will burst through tree canopies and bushes to surprise unsuspecting victims. Soars for long periods, occasionally using a flap-flap-glide motion.

HABITAT: Forest edges and wooded glades.

DISTRIBUTION: Widespread across the United States. Range extends to Mexico in winter.

Red-tailed Hawk
Buteo jamaicensis

LENGTH: 19"

DESCRIPTION: A common hawk that shows many variations from all-dark to very pale individuals. Adults have a yellow and black beak. A white- or black-tipped red tail is evident in all races except one with an off-white tail. Upper parts are differing shades of brown; underwing primary and secondary feathers are usually barred. It is in the body and underwing that the pale to dark variation is most common. Seen from below the wings appear quite broad and the tail long. Juvenile lacks the red tail and is more barred but can still show color variations. Legs are yellow in all ages.

VOICE: A typically harsh raptor-like elongated scream, *skeeerrrrrrrr.*

BEHAVIOR: Most often seen sitting on a telegraph post or soaring in circles high in the sky, before dropping down with talons open to catch prey.

HABITAT: Fields and open grassland.

DISTRIBUTION: Resident in much of North America. Breeding populations are found north of Iowa over the border into Canada and as far north as Alaska.

Virginia Rail
Rallus limicola

LENGTH: 9.5"

DESCRIPTION: A medium-sized rail. Adult has a comparatively long curved orange bill with a dark line running down its center, a dark crown offset with blue-gray cheek patches and orange eyes. Overall body color is a reddish brown, with black and white barring towards the rear. Tail is short and often held upright, showing off the white undertail. Legs are orange. Juvenile is darker brown and the head appears to have a dirty white supercilium that continues around the cheeks, which are dark to the throat.

VOICE: A series of *kiwip-kiwip-kekewip* calls which often change in tone midway through.

BEHAVIOR: Likes to feed in shallow muddy water in search of insects. Will often feed in full view although dives for cover if disturbed.

HABITAT: Boggy marshland with good cover.

DISTRIBUTION: Winters along the coast from North Carolina to British Columbia. Seen year round from California north along the west coast. Summering birds can be found in a swath across the United States from Maine to Idaho.

61

SORA
Porzana carolina

LENGTH: 8.75"

DESCRIPTION: A small crake. Adults have a short, stout yellow bill, leading to a black face patch and eye. To the rear of the eye is a small white spot. A black crown stripe breaks up an otherwise brown crown, cheeks and breast are blue-gray, leading to black and white barring. The back and upper tail are mostly brown, with many feathers having a black center and white edge. Undertail has a buff center edged in white. Legs are light green-yellow. Juvenile is a more buff color and lighter on the back. It lacks the blue-gray front and the only black on the head is the crown stripe.

VOICE: A shrill, almost raptor-like *kewick* and more tuneful longer *tee-te-te-eeee.*

BEHAVIOR: A quite bold bird which is happy feeding out in full view in the wet mud around the edges of reeds. Nevertheless expert at hiding and will scurry away if disturbed.

HABITAT: Marshland and muddy edges of lakes.

DISTRIBUTION: Breeds from Oklahoma north to Canada. Winters along the coast from North Carolina to California.

Sandhill Crane
Grus canadensis

LENGTH: 46"

DESCRIPTION: A tall graceful bird with a long neck. Adults have a large black pointed bill. A bright red patch extends from the base of the bill to the crown and encompasses an orange eye. The rest of the body is pale gray, often showing brown patches as plumage becomes worn. Tail is formed by a series of plumes. Legs are long and black. When in flight shows a two-toned gray-white underwing with black edges to the primaries and secondaries. Juvenile lacks the red crown and is a mixture of brown and gray, depending on age, the gray becoming more dominant as the bird matures.

VOICE: A rattling *hakrrr* repeated several times.

BEHAVIOR: A social bird that can be found in large noisy groups, often out in open fields and almost always on the move foraging for food.

HABITAT: Open fields and boggy grassland.

DISTRIBUTION: Commoner in the summer in Canada from Manitoba north to islands off Nunavut. When migrating seen in central to western states from Nebraska to British Columbia. Winters in Mexico.

American Avocet
Recurvirostra americana

LENGTH: 17.5"

DESCRIPTION: A striking elegant shorebird. In summer the adult has a long, thin, slightly upturned black bill, usually more upturned in females than males. Black eye with a pale eye-ring. Head, neck and breast are a bronzy red; wings are black with a white wing-bar. In flight the underwing is mainly white with black primaries; the rest of the body is white. Legs are long and pale gray. Winter birds lack the coloration on the head, neck and breast, which are off-white. Juvenile is much like summer adult but duller, with coloration extending only from the crown down the back of the neck.

VOICE: A high pitched, repeated *pleek*.

BEHAVIOR: Wades through water, often up to its body, sifting its bill from side to side searching for small invertebrates on which to feed.

HABITAT: Marshland and muddy fringes of lakes.

DISTRIBUTION: Breeding colonies are found from New Mexico north to southern Canada. Wintering birds are found mainly around the coast of Mexico.

American Golden Plover
Pluvialis dominica

LENGTH: 10.5"

DESCRIPTION: A dark but colorful plover. In the summer adult the bill is small, pointed and black. Plumage is black from the base of the bill past the cheeks, neck, breast and underside. The crown, rear of the neck and back are all gold pricked with black spotting of various sizes and the tail is barred. Clear white bands extend from the forehead over each eye, behind the ear coverts and down the side of the neck, where they widen and continue to the top of the breast, not quite meeting in the middle. Legs are dark gray. In flight the underwing is light gray. Winter adult and juvenile lack significant color and appear rather gray but browner on the back, with a prominent white supercilium.

VOICE: A high-pitched *queek* alarm call and a *quwee-wee* call given in flight.

BEHAVIOR: Likes to feed in the open and is often on the move, feeding for a short while in one spot before running to another position.

HABITAT: Tundra and coastal lagoons.

DISTRIBUTION: Breeds from Alaska east to Baffin Island in northern Canada. Migratory birds pass through many of the central and eastern states of the United States.

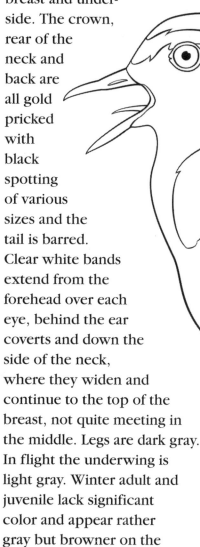

69

Killdeer
Charadrius vociferus

LENGTH: 10.5"

DESCRIPTION: A mid-sized plover. Adult has two black bands across the upper breast, the higher of which forms a full band around the neck, above this is a white collar, the bill is dark, a large black eye with an orange ring sits in the middle of a collage of white, brown and black patches, the crown and back are light brown, underside is white, but the surprise comes in flight when an orange rump and tail are shown, the latter being edged black and white. Legs are pale and quite long for a plover. Juvenile is a duller version of the adult but still retains the breast-bands.

VOICE: A shrill *de-dee-a* in flight, as well as a repeated *teeweet*. At times it appears to call its own name.

BEHAVIOR: Mostly found amongst short vegetation, where it can easily disappear if disturbed. Like many plovers it is frequently on the move in search of food.

HABITAT: Short stubble fields, open farmland and low grasslands.

DISTRIBUTION: Populations can be found year round in the southern half of the United States up to Virginia in the east to Washington in the west. Summering birds are seen in the Northwest Territories.

Short-billed Dowitcher

Limnodromus griseus

LENGTH: 11"

DESCRIPTION: A sturdy shorebird. Summer adult form has a long, dark, pointed bill which makes the head appear small. A brown eye stripe dissects a dark eye and a white supercilium makes the brown crown stand out. The throat down to the underside is orange, whilst the undertail is paler with black spotting. Back and tail are mottled brown. Legs are long and pale. Winter adult form lacks the orange coloring and is instead pale gray-brown with a white underside. Juvenile is a washed out buffy version of the summer adult.

VOICE: A fluty *tew-tew-tew* call repeated several times.

BEHAVIOR: Patrols the shallows, sometimes in large flocks, "drilling" its bill in to the wet mud to draw out a tasty meal.

HABITAT: Coastal waters and mud flats

DISTRIBUTION: Modest populations are found summering in Canada, from the south of Hudson Bay to Alberta.

In winter can be seen around the coast from Oregon to Delaware.

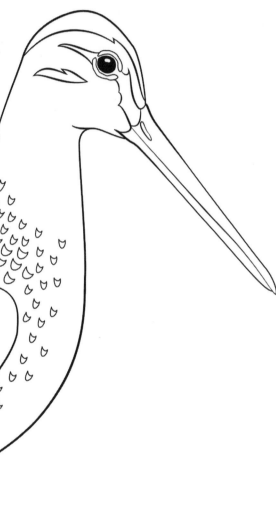

Spotted Sandpiper
Actitis macularius

LENGTH: 7.5"

DESCRIPTION: A small shorebird which often bobs its tail. Summer adult has a white throat, breast and underside covered in black spots, which decrease in number down the body. Pointed orange bill has a black tip. A black eye with white ring and supercilium stands out against a pale brown head. The back is brown peppered with black flecks rather than spots. Wings are two-toned in flight and appear rather short; legs are pale. Winter adult and juvenile lack black spots or flecks, being pale brown with white underparts; juveniles show some brown barring on the wings and back.

VOICE: A bubbly *peep-pe-pe-peep*.

BEHAVIOR: A bit of a loner, found on its own feeding on the banks of ponds and lakes quietly bobbing up and down. Flies off calling when disturbed.

HABITAT: Lakes, coastal waters and man-made expanses of water.

DISTRIBUTION: Summering birds are found throughout much of the United States and Canada from Arizona north to Alaska and east to Quebec. Wintering birds are found from Florida along the coast to Mexico.

75

Ruddy Turnstone
Arenaria interpres

LENGTH: 9.5"

DESCRIPTION: A mid-sized shorebird. Summer adult is mottled black and white from the breast up. The short pointed bill is black, as is the crown. The back is black broken up by a rich bronze. When in flight more white patches become apparent including one along the back close to a dark rump and black and white tail. Legs are orange.

Winter adult and juvenile are similar and lack the brightness of the summer plumage, being replaced by a mixture of light and dark brown, juvenile is slightly more patterned than winter adult.

VOICE: A repetitive *chee-wit*.

BEHAVIOR: As its name suggests, forages around shorelines, fields and coastal verges using its bill to turn stones in search of food.

HABITAT: Shorelines and rocky bays.

DISTRIBUTION: Breeds around the Queen Elizabeth Islands of Canada and in Northern Alaska. Wintering birds are seen around most of the southern coastline of the United States. Rarely seen inland.

Red-necked Phalarope
Phalaropus lobatus

LENGTH: 7.75"

DESCRIPTION: A small delicate shorebird. Female has a fine pointed black bill and sooty head, with a small white patch at the front of the eye, white throat and a rich red neck. A slate gray band around the breast and shoulders spreads down the body and is broken up on the back by two orange bars. The underside is white and a white wingbar is visible in flight along with a two-toned underwing. Legs are dark. Male is duller than the female, with a darker eye patch and crown and less of a pronounced red neck; the rest of the body is similar. In winter both sexes lose their color, reverting to mottled gray backs and white undersides with darker eye patches and crowns. Juvenile is similar to winter adult but a warmer brown and black.

VOICE: A short throaty *chip*.

BEHAVIOR: These birds are happy either on a still secluded lake or feeding on vegetation floating out in the open ocean.

HABITAT: Open ocean and large vegetated lakes.

DISTRIBUTION: Breeds across northern Canada from Alaska to Newfoundland. Can be seen anywhere around the coasts of America and Canada during migration but spends the winter out in the ocean.

79

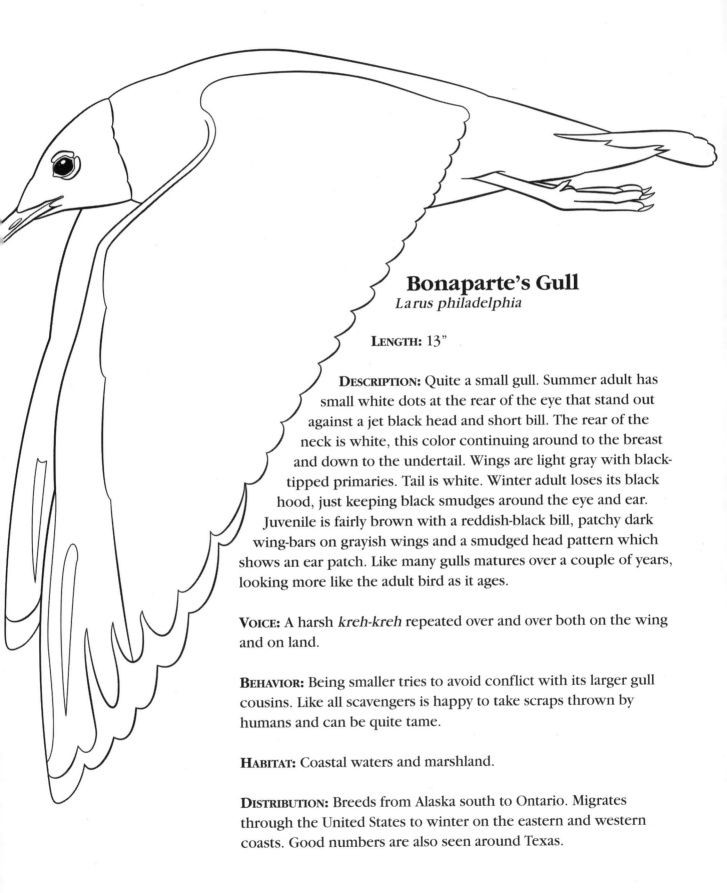

Bonaparte's Gull
Larus philadelphia

LENGTH: 13"

DESCRIPTION: Quite a small gull. Summer adult has small white dots at the rear of the eye that stand out against a jet black head and short bill. The rear of the neck is white, this color continuing around to the breast and down to the undertail. Wings are light gray with black-tipped primaries. Tail is white. Winter adult loses its black hood, just keeping black smudges around the eye and ear. Juvenile is fairly brown with a reddish-black bill, patchy dark wing-bars on grayish wings and a smudged head pattern which shows an ear patch. Like many gulls matures over a couple of years, looking more like the adult bird as it ages.

VOICE: A harsh *kreh-kreh* repeated over and over both on the wing and on land.

BEHAVIOR: Being smaller tries to avoid conflict with its larger gull cousins. Like all scavengers is happy to take scraps thrown by humans and can be quite tame.

HABITAT: Coastal waters and marshland.

DISTRIBUTION: Breeds from Alaska south to Ontario. Migrates through the United States to winter on the eastern and western coasts. Good numbers are also seen around Texas.

Caspian Tern
Sterna caspia

LENGTH: 21"

DESCRIPTION: A large bulky tern. Summer adult has huge heavy red bill with a dark tip. A black cap stretches from just below the eye to the back of the head and may appear to form a slight crest; cap becomes lighter and flecked white in winter. Wings and back are mainly pale gray except the primaries which appear darker. Underside is white and legs are dark. Juvenile is similar to winter adult but browner on the back and with an orange bill.

VOICE: A harsh and rasping repeated *kerrk*.

BEHAVIOR: At first glance, could be confused for a gull due to its size and slower, steady flight pattern. Can be seen on either fresh or salt water, often patrolling above the water before dropping down to catch a fish.

HABITAT: Anywhere from the open ocean to coastal shores and large freshwater lakes.

DISTRIBUTION: Small populations breed in southern Canada around Lake Winnipeg and east to Alberta. Migratory birds can be seen inland further south to the coast of Florida. Seen year round along the east coast to Mexico.

Black Skimmer
Rynchops niger

LENGTH: 18"

DESCRIPTION: Unmistakable in flight or at rest, the summer adult has a large red and black bill which looks deformed, with the lower mandible projecting past the upper. A white forehead, breast and underside contrast with a black cap, rear neck and back. The tail is white with a black central band. Long wings that project past the tail are also mainly black, with white edges to the secondaries. Legs are orange. Winter adult has a black cap and white collar and the bill loses some brightness. Juvenile has underside similar to adult; upperparts are more like winter adult but browner with feather edges dirty white. The bill is much duller.

VOICE: A deep *yar-yar-yup*, with single *yup* calls also made.

BEHAVIOR: Mostly seen flying above water like a tern before dropping down and flying with the lower bill just skimming the surface. When at rest birds can sometimes be seen outstretched resting their head and bills almost as if they were too heavy to hold up.

HABITAT: Coastal waters and shallow lagoons.

DISTRIBUTION: Rarely seen inland. Modest numbers year round from North Carolina to Mexico.

Atlantic Puffin
Fratercula arctica

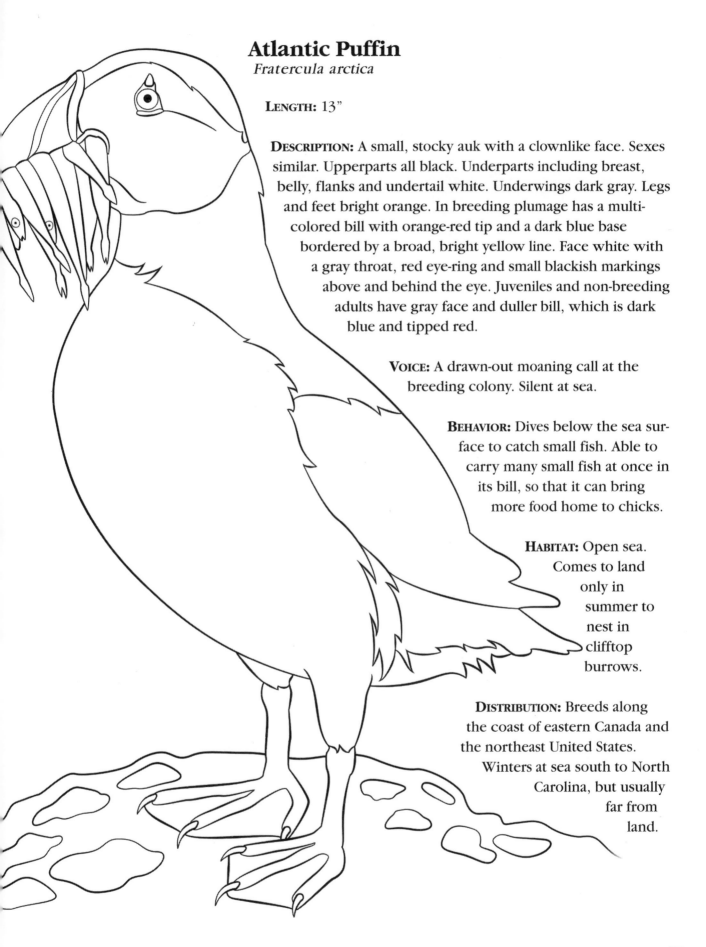

LENGTH: 13"

DESCRIPTION: A small, stocky auk with a clownlike face. Sexes similar. Upperparts all black. Underparts including breast, belly, flanks and undertail white. Underwings dark gray. Legs and feet bright orange. In breeding plumage has a multi-colored bill with orange-red tip and a dark blue base bordered by a broad, bright yellow line. Face white with a gray throat, red eye-ring and small blackish markings above and behind the eye. Juveniles and non-breeding adults have gray face and duller bill, which is dark blue and tipped red.

VOICE: A drawn-out moaning call at the breeding colony. Silent at sea.

BEHAVIOR: Dives below the sea surface to catch small fish. Able to carry many small fish at once in its bill, so that it can bring more food home to chicks.

HABITAT: Open sea. Comes to land only in summer to nest in clifftop burrows.

DISTRIBUTION: Breeds along the coast of eastern Canada and the northeast United States. Winters at sea south to North Carolina, but usually far from land.

Band-tailed Pigeon
Columba fasciata

LENGTH: 14.5"

DESCRIPTION: A relatively large pigeon with a pointed yellow black-tipped bill. A dark eye is surrounded by a pinkish-red eye ring. Head and breast are a pale gray–mauve. A white rear neck collar tops a patch of metallic green. The main body, rump and wings are slate gray; primaries and some secondaries are dark. The long tail is spread in flight. The final third of the tail is pale, giving a banded effect. Legs are yellow. Juvenile lacks the adult body color and is two-toned gray overall. Bill and legs are similar to the adult but paler.

VOICE: A haunting *whoo-who-whoo* usually given while perched.

BEHAVIOR: Will gather in large flocks, bursting from cover with loud wing claps if disturbed. Feeds in trees or on the ground.

HABITAT: Woodlands, parks and suburban gardens. Spreading to more built up areas.

DISTRIBUTION: Found mainly in the west from British Columbia to New Mexico.

Mourning Dove
Zenaida macroura

LENGTH: 12"

DESCRIPTION: A graceful and slim dove. Adult is a warm light brown-buff color overall, with a slightly rusty crown. Dark eyes are ringed by a pale blue-gray eye-ring, the bill is short and gray, and back and wings are slightly rufous with several black spots. Shows a gray underwing when in flight. Tail is diamond shaped with a white edge and dark sub-terminal bands which do not stretch as far as the central point of the tail. Legs are pink. Juvenile is similar to adult but paler and more barred around the face and breast.

VOICE: A mournful *Coo-whoo-coo-coo* made while perched.

BEHAVIOR: Mainly ground feeding, will forage amongst vegetation looking for seeds. Flocks often seen perched on telegraph poles and wires.

HABITAT: Regularly found in open grassland, parks and suburban gardens.

DISTRIBUTION: A common dove found year round throughout much of the United States from Washington to Maine, with some birds moving north into southern Canada to breed.

Yellow-billed Cuckoo
Coccyzus americanus

LENGTH: 12"

DESCRIPTION: The most colorful of the cuckoos found in North America. Adult has a mainly yellow bill, which is quite bulky with a black line above. Eye is dark with a prominent yellow eye ring. Lower cheeks, throat and underside are all white; crown, nape, back and tail are brown apart from the outer tail feathers, which are black with white edges and tips.

Much of the wing is a rich chestnut color which is also visible on the underwing in the primaries and secondaries, the remainder being white. When just fledged the juvenile lacks the yellow on the bill.

VOICE: A series of low quick *tak-tak-tak* and slower *kawlp-kawlp* calls.

BEHAVIOR: Tends to move through dense foliage in search of grubs rather than sit out in the open.

HABITAT: Tall scrub and open woodland.

DISTRIBUTION: Found in summer months from Maine south to Texas and inland to Montana. Rarely seen further east or north. Not seen in winter.

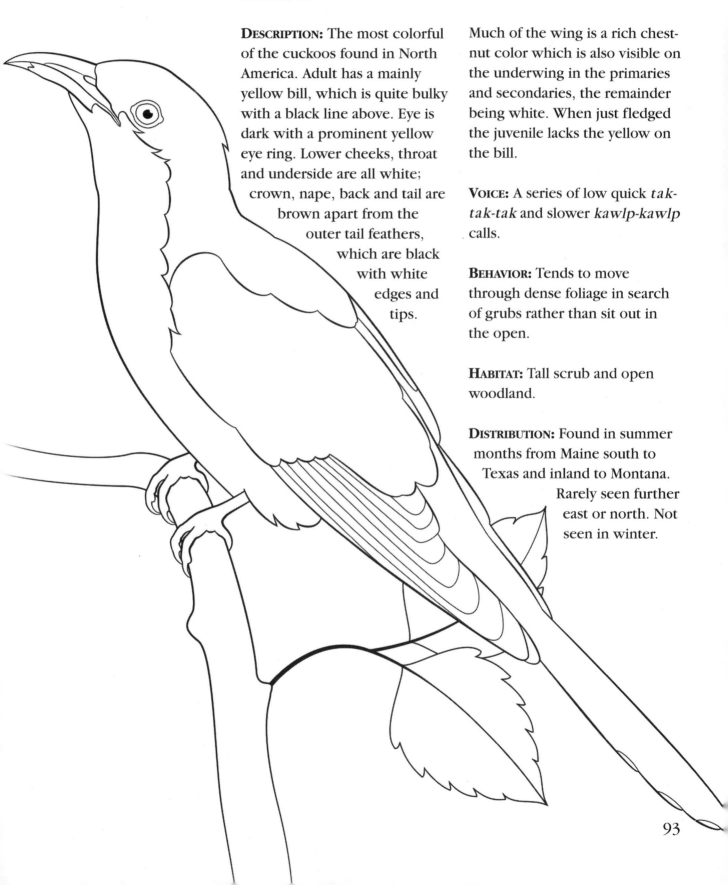

Greater Roadrunner
Geococcyx californianus

LENGTH: 23"

DESCRIPTION: A peculiar fowl-like bird. Male is fairly nondescript being brown and mottled. The only striking color is a patch of skin behind the eye that is a mix of blue, white and red. A dark crown is often raised to a rough crest. The bill is stout. Underside is dirty buff, tail is long and dark with a little white edging. In flight the underwing is black. Legs are long and light gray. Female is even duller than the male, with less of a crest and no red and white behind the eye, just a small patch of blue.

VOICE: Makes a slow and drawn out series of *coos* that seem to get slower and longer as they go, these are similar to a toy running out of batteries.

BEHAVIOR: Runs along the ground and over rocks, sometimes in quite strange positions, looking for small reptiles. Likes to sunbathe on rocks or posts.

HABITAT: Deserts and dry open grasslands.

DISTRIBUTION: Mainly confined to the dry southern states of America, from Arkansas to southern Nevada.

Barn Owl
Tyto alba

LENGTH: 16"

DESCRIPTION: A silent and ghostly owl. Sexes alike but male is paler. Large dark eyes and a hooked pale beak sit in a white heart-shaped face. Breast down to under-tail is white with sporadic small black dots to the edge of the breast. Crown and back are a mixture of pale orange-buff with darker brown patches and fine barring, especially in the wings. In flight the underside is all white, giving a ghostly appearance. Legs are quite long and partially feathered white. The talons are dark and sharp.

VOICE: A harsh and drawn-out *creeeeshh*, which can carry quite some distance.

BEHAVIOR: Hunts at night, silently patrolling fields and roadside verges in search of small mammals. Will hunt in daylight when it has young to feed.

HABITAT: Open farmland and grassland

DISTRIBUTION: A resident bird found throughout much of America, from Oregon in the west, across to Virginia in the east and south down to Texas.

97

Burrowing Owl
Athene cunicularia

LENGTH: 9.5"

DESCRIPTION: A small, heavily spotted owl. Adult has large yellow eyes, a small pale bill and a white eyebrow stripe that dips to the base of the beak, giving a surprised expression. Apart from the pale throat and white undertail, the rest of the body is pale brown with white spots. Legs are long and pale. Some races appear darker and more streaked. Juvenile is much plainer than the adult and lacks the white spots, with rich creamy breast and underside.

VOICE: A fairly sad repeated *coo-cooo* and a shrill *wick wick wick* call.

BEHAVIOR: Often seen on the ground or perched on a lookout post bobbing up and down on its long legs. Will fly quite close to the ground before swooping up to a viewpoint. Nests on the ground in disused burrows.

HABITAT: Found mainly on open prairies and grasslands.

DISTRIBUTION: Two populations are found in the United States, one from Mexico across the border and up to North Dakota, the other in Florida.

99

Long-eared Owl
Asio otus

LENGTH: 15"

DESCRIPTION: Cryptic plumage that is supremely camouflaged against branches and tree trunks. Upperparts mostly gray-brown with rufous and buff streaks, bars and spots. Underparts rufous and buff with darker grayish barring and streaking. Rufous patch on the primaries shows especially in flight. Facial disk white in the center, bordered black and rufous on outer areas. Eyes orange. Long ear-tufts rufous and black.

VOICE: Adult makes a loud *hoot*, juvenile sounds like a squeaky gate.

BEHAVIOR: Strictly nocturnal. Roosts in trees by day, disguising itself as a trunk or branch. At night hunts by flying and swooping on prey.

HABITAT: Roosts in forests and thickets, hunts among trees or over open areas such as fields and meadows.

DISTRIBUTION: Breeds in southern Canada and northern and western United States. In winter found in much of the United States except the southeast.

101

Common Nighthawk
Chordeiles minor

LENGTH: 9"

DESCRIPTION: A brown-gray bird with a distinctive shape, a very small dark bill, black eyes, slim but fairly long pointed wings and an obviously notched tail. When at rest the wings extend past the end of the tail. The main flight feathers of the male are unbarred with white wing patches. A large white throat patch and white tail band are also evident. Female similar to the male but lacks the white tail band and the throat and wing patches are creamy buff. Juvenile is similar to female but slightly paler and with a barred throat patch.

VOICE: A nasal *pee* or *pee-ik*.

BEHAVIOR: Flies from early evening but can also be seen during the day. Hawks insects high in the air. Perches on open branches or fence posts.

HABITAT: Large open areas from plains to open woodland.

DISTRIBUTION: Breeds in much of Central and North America but winters mainly in South America.

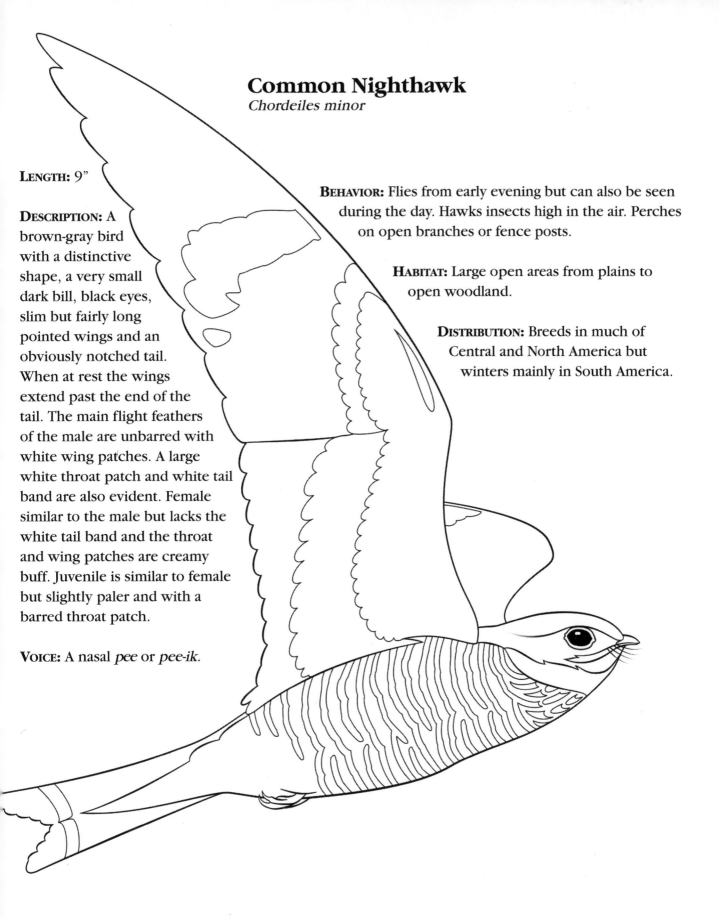

103

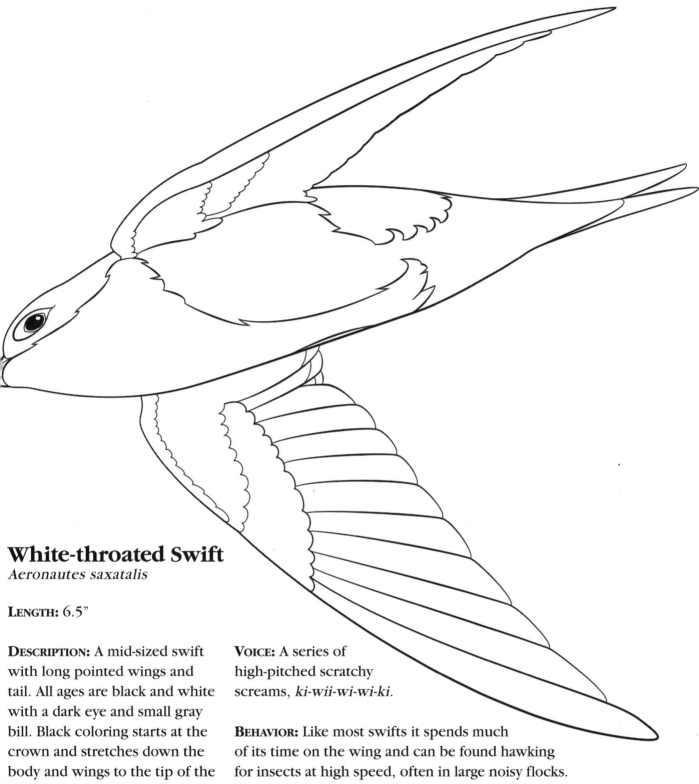

White-throated Swift
Aeronautes saxatalis

LENGTH: 6.5"

DESCRIPTION: A mid-sized swift with long pointed wings and tail. All ages are black and white with a dark eye and small gray bill. Black coloring starts at the crown and stretches down the body and wings to the tip of the tail; the underwing is also black. White coloring starts beneath the eye and continues down the throat and partway down the breast. Secondary tips are also white and have two white side patches directly behind them.

VOICE: A series of high-pitched scratchy screams, *ki-wii-wi-wi-ki*.

BEHAVIOR: Like most swifts it spends much of its time on the wing and can be found hawking for insects at high speed, often in large noisy flocks.

HABITAT: Mountains and cliffs.

DISTRIBUTION: Resident from western Texas up to southern Nevada. Summering birds are found as far north as British Columbia and inland to South Dakota.

Ruby-throated Hummingbird
Archilochus colubris

LENGTH: 3.75"

DESCRIPTION: A little gem. The male has a thin black bill, a vivid green crown, back and tail although outer-tail can show some black and white banding. A black eye patch and white breastband help set off a bright red throat. The underside is off-white with a touch of green and wings are black-green above, pale below. Legs are black. Female retains green on the back and head although head is a little duller. A dark spot behind the eye and white throat replace the red and black of the male. Juvenile is similar to female but with a shorter bill.

VOICE: A trill *ch-i-i-i-ci-ci-ch-i-i.*

BEHAVIOR: An aerial genius, this bird can stop on a dime. It will fly up, down, backwards or forwards or hover at natural and artificial food sources.

HABITAT: Parks, open woodland and suburban gardens

DISTRIBUTION: A summer breeder in much of the eastern half of the United States and Southern Canada, from Louisiana up to North Dakota and along to Alberta. Can be seen as far north as Nova Scotia on the east coast. Winters in southern Mexico and South America.

107

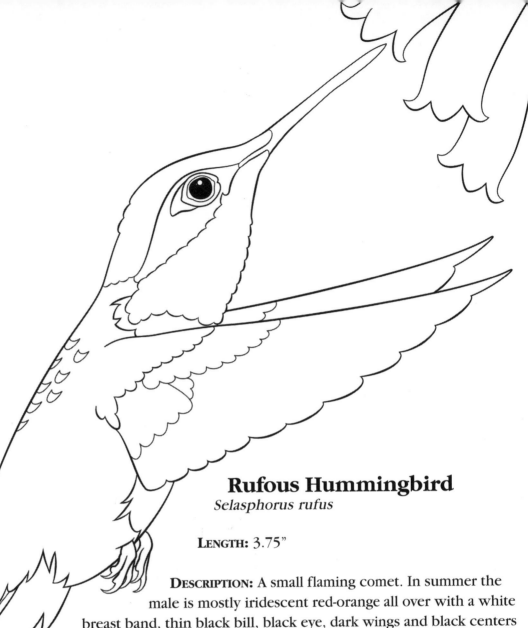

Rufous Hummingbird
Selasphorus rufus

LENGTH: 3.75"

DESCRIPTION: A small flaming comet. In summer the male is mostly iridescent red-orange all over with a white breast band, thin black bill, black eye, dark wings and black centers to the tail feathers. Female is green on the crown and back with a pale belly and throat, and some orange spotting, sides and tail are tinged orange and tail feathers have black markings and white tips. Juvenile is much like female.

VOICE: A harsh *pzee-pzee-churrp-churrp*, and a series of *pzip* or *pzup* calls.

BEHAVIOR: A regular visitor to artificial feeding stations as well as natural nectar sources. Becomes quite aggressive to others when defending a particularly good feeding spot.

HABITAT: Open woodland, parks and suburban gardens.

DISTRIBUTION: Birds summer on the west coast from Oregon north to southern Alaska. When migrating can be seen inland to Montana and as far south as Texas. Winters in South America.

Belted Kingfisher
Megaceryle alcyon

LENGTH: 13"

DESCRIPTION: A magnificent fish-catcher. Male has a large dark pointed bill, dark eye with a conspicuous white spot just in front of it and a white collar beneath a blue-gray head with a messy crest. Breast band and back are blue-gray, short tail is blue-gray barred white, breast and underside are white, wings are blue-gray with several white patches and a pale underwing. Legs are dark. Female much like the male with a lower red breast band and red sides at the base of the wings. Juvenile is similar to female but has a broken red band and a much darker upper breast band; the crown is untidy but not as obviously crested at the adults.

VOICE: A harsh, rattling *tyrrrrr* repeated several times.

BEHAVIOR: Like many kingfishers can often be found perched above water surveying the area below. Also seen hovering above the water before plunging down to catch a fish.

HABITAT: Lakes and rivers.

DISTRIBUTION: A common bird throughout most of North America, resident from Massachusetts to Washington. Breeding birds are also found further north, from Newfoundland to Alaska north of the Yukon.

Coloring Guide

Californian Quail
Callipepla californica–page 5

Northern Bobwhite
Colinus virginianus–page 7

Wild Turkey
Meleagris gallopavo–page 9

Spruce Grouse
Falcipennis canadensis–page 11

Ring-necked Pheasant
Phasianus colchicus–page 13

Wood Duck
Aix sponsa–page 15

American Wigeon
Anas americana–page 17

Mallard
Anas platyrhynchos–page 19

Blue-winged Teal
Anas discors–page 21

Northern Shoveler
Anas clypeata–page 23

Hooded Merganser
Lophodytes cucullatus–page 25

Red-breasted Merganser
Mergus serrator–page 27

Ruddy Duck
Oxyura jamaicensis–page 29

Common Loon
Gavia immer–page 31

Northern Fulmar
Fulmarus glacialis–page 33

Pied-billed Grebe
Podilymbus podiceps–page 35

White-faced Ibis
Plegadis chihi–page 37

American Bittern
Botaurus lentiginosus–page 39

Green Heron
Butorides virescens–page 41

Cattle Egret
Bubulcus ibis–page 43

Great Blue Heron
Ardea herodias–page 45

Brown Pelican
Pelecanus occidentalis–page 47

Double-crested Cormorant
Phalacrocorax auritus–page 49

Turkey Vulture
Cathartes aura–page 51

American Kestrel
Falco sparverius–page 53

Bald Eagle
Haliaeetus leucocephalus–page 55

Cooper's Hawk
Accipiter cooperii–page 57

Red-tailed Hawk
Buteo jamaicensis–page 59

Virginia Rail
Rallus limicola–page 61

Sora
Porzana carolina–page 63

Sandhill Crane
Grus canadensis–page 65

American Avocet
Recurvirostra americana–page 67

American Golden Plover
Pluvialis dominica–page 69

Killdeer

Charadrius vociferus–page 71

Short-billed Dowitcher

Limnodromus griseusc–page 73

Spotted Sandpiper

Actitis macularius–page 75

Ruddy Turnstone

Arenaria interpres–page 77

Red-necked Phalarope

Phalaropus lobatus–page 79

Bonaparte's Gull

Larus philadelphia–page 81

Caspian Tern

Sterna caspia–page 83

Black Skimmer
Rynchops niger–page 85

Atlantic Puffin
Fratercula arctica–page 87

Band-tailed Pigeon
Columba fasciata–page 89

Mourning Dove
Zenaida macroura–page 91

Yellow-billed Cuckoo
Coccyzus americanus–page 93

Greater Roadrunner
Geococcyx californianus–page 95

Barn Owl
Tyto alba–page 97

Burrowing Owl
Athene cunicularia–page 99

Long-eared Owl
Asio otus–page 101

Common Nighthawk
Chordeiles minor–page 103

White-throated Swift
Aeronautes saxatalis–page 105

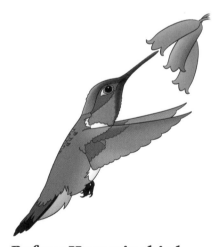

Ruby-throated Hummingbird
Archilochus colubris–page 107

Rufous Hummingbird
Selasphorus rufus–page 109

Belted Kingfisher
Megaceryle alcyon–page 111

Lewis's Woodpecker
Melanerpes lewis—page 129

Yellow-bellied Sapsucker
Sphyrapicus varius—page 131

Northern Flicker
Colaptes auratus—page 133

Pileated Woodpecker
Dryocopus pileatus—page 135

Vermilion Flycatcher
Pyrocephalus rubinus—page 137

Western Kingbird
Tyrannus verticalis—page 139

Yellow-throated Vireo
Vireo flavifrons—page 141

Blue Jay
Cyanocitta cristata–page 143

Western Scrub Jay
Aphelocoma californica–page 145

Black-billed Magpie
Pica hudsonia–page 147

Clark's Nutcracker
Nucifraga columbiana–page 149

Cedar Waxwing
Bombycilla cedrorum–page 151

Black-capped Chickadee
Parus atricapillus–page 153

Tufted Titmouse
Parus bicolor–page 155

Verdin
Auriparus flaviceps–page 157

Purple Martin
Progne subis–page 159

Barn Swallow
Hirundo rustica–page 161

Cliff Swallow
Petrochelidon pyrrhonota–page 163

Horned Lark
Eremophila alpestris–page 165

Golden-crowned Kinglet
Regulus satrapa–page 167

House Wren
Troglodytes aedon–page 169

Blue-gray Gnatcatcher
Polioptila caerulea–page 171

Red-breasted Nuthatch
Sitta canadensis–page 173

White-breasted Nuthatch
Sitta carolinensis–page 175

Brown Creeper
Certhia americana–page 177

Gray Catbird
Dumetella carolinensis–page 179

Brown Thrasher
Toxostoma rufum–page 181

Varied Thrush
Ixoreus naevius–page 183

124

Western Bluebird
Sialia mexicana–page 185

Wood Thrush
Hylocichla mustelina–page 187

American Robin
Turdus migratorius–page 189

American Goldfinch
Carduelis tristis–page 191

House Finch
Carpodacus mexicanus–page 193

Evening Grosbeak
Hesperiphona vespertina–page 195

Yellow Warbler
Dendroica petechia–page 197

Cape May Warbler
Dendroica tigrina–page 199

Yellow-rumped Warbler
Dendroica coronata–page 201

Townsend's Warbler
Dendroica townsendi–page 203

Black-and-white Warbler
Mniotilta varia–page 205

American Redstart
Setophaga ruticilla–page 207

Common Yellowthroat
Geothlypis trichas–page 209

Yellow-breasted Chat
Icteria virens–page 211

Baltimore Oriole
Icterus galbula–page 213

Bullock's Oriole
Icterus bullockii–page 215

Red-winged Blackbird
Agelaius phoeniceus–page 217

Western Meadowlark
Sturnella neglecta–page 219

Bobolink
Dolichonyx oryzivorus–page 221

White-crowned Sparrow
Zonotrichia leucophrys–page 223

American Tree Sparrow
Spizella arborea–page 225

Eastern Towhee
Pipilo erythrophthalmus–page 227

Dickcissel
Spiza americana–page 229

Black-headed Grosbeak
Pheucticus melanocephalus–page 231

Northern Cardinal
Cardinalis cardinalis–page 233

Blue Grosbeak
Passerina caerulea–page 235

Lazuli Bunting
Passerina amoena–page 237

Painted Bunting
Passerina amoena–page 239

Lewis's Woodpecker
Melanerpes lewis

LENGTH: 10.5"

DESCRIPTION: A bright, glossy woodpecker. Adult has a dark, stocky and pointed bill and dark eye surrounded by a red face patch. Crown and area around and under the throat is dark, a full pale gray collar extends to the top of the breast. Underside is red and undertail is dark. The back, tail and wings are glossy black-green with a dark under-wing. Legs are pale gray. Juvenile has a dark face and dirty brown front, with some red showing through depending on age; the back is still dark green but not as glossy.

VOICE: A chattering call almost like a squeaky hinge.

BEHAVIOR: Tends to creep around the trunks of trees and out along the branches in search of insects. Like all woodpeckers drums on trees to attract other birds and whilst nest building.

HABITAT: Mature woodland.

DISTRIBUTION: A resident bird confined to western states from New Mexico to Washington. Breeding birds move slightly further north to the southern part of British Columbia.

Yellow-bellied Sapsucker
Sphyrapicus varius

LENGTH: 8.5"

DESCRIPTION: One of several sapsuckers. Male has a red crown encased with a black surround. A white stripe from the back of the eye and one from the base of the bill are split by a black eye stripe giving a masked effect. A black breast bib has a red throat patch in the middle, underside is creamy yellow, and the back, wings and tail are black with white patches, some such as the wing patches being quite significant. Legs pale. Female is similar to male but paler with a white throat, and narrower black stripes on the head. Juvenile is similar to female but lacks any red and thus appears darker overall.

VOICE: A series of nasal *meee* calls.

BEHAVIOR: Usually seen stuck to a tree trunk making small holes from which it takes the sap.

HABITAT: Open woodland.

DISTRIBUTION: Winters from Mexico to North Carolina. Moves further north and west to breed fom Maine to Canada and Alaska.

Northern Flicker
Colaptes auratus

LENGTH: 12.5"

DESCRIPTION: Two distinct races – western and eastern – both have a very slightly down-curved dark bill and a white rump and are covered with black spots on the breast and barring on the back. In the west the male has a red mustache stripe, light gray cheeks and throat, a gray-brown crown, a black breast bib and pale underside. The back is light brown, wing tips and tail are black with orange centers and a reddish-orange underwing is visible in flight. Western females lack the mustache stripe. Males in the east have a black mustache stripe, light rufous cheeks and throat, light gray crown and nape with a red patch to the rear. The underside is more buff, and underwing is yellow. Females lack the mustache stripe but still have a red patch at back of the head.

VOICE: Repetitive *wik-wik-wik* and a high pitched *keyer*.

BEHAVIOR: A ground feeder. Will crouch low to forage in short grass, flushing out ants.

HABITAT: Parks, open woodland and grassland close to trees.

DISTRIBUTION: Resident throughout the United States. Summering birds also found from Labrador to mid-Alaska.

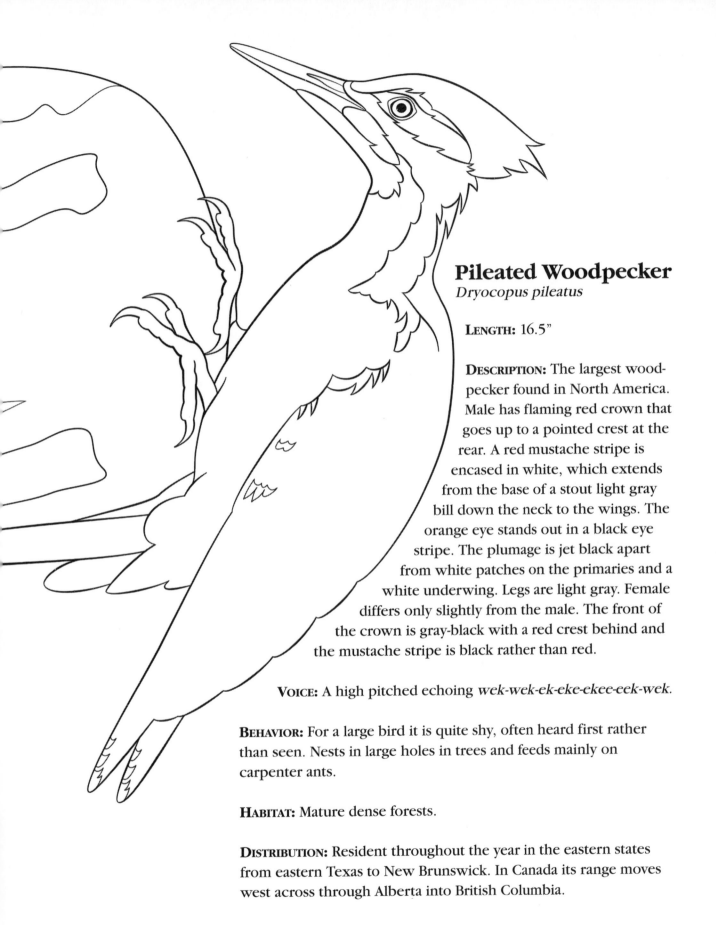

Pileated Woodpecker
Dryocopus pileatus

LENGTH: 16.5"

DESCRIPTION: The largest wood-pecker found in North America. Male has flaming red crown that goes up to a pointed crest at the rear. A red mustache stripe is encased in white, which extends from the base of a stout light gray bill down the neck to the wings. The orange eye stands out in a black eye stripe. The plumage is jet black apart from white patches on the primaries and a white underwing. Legs are light gray. Female differs only slightly from the male. The front of the crown is gray-black with a red crest behind and the mustache stripe is black rather than red.

VOICE: A high pitched echoing *wek-wek-ek-eke-ekee-eek-wek*.

BEHAVIOR: For a large bird it is quite shy, often heard first rather than seen. Nests in large holes in trees and feeds mainly on carpenter ants.

HABITAT: Mature dense forests.

DISTRIBUTION: Resident throughout the year in the eastern states from eastern Texas to New Brunswick. In Canada its range moves west across through Alberta into British Columbia.

Vermilion Flycatcher
Pyrocephalus rubinus

LENGTH: 6"

DESCRIPTION:
Beautifully
garish. Male
has a small
black pointed bill,
the black coloring
contining through the
eye around the nape and
down the whole of the
back, rounded wings and
short tail. The slight crest,
crown, throat, breast and
whole underside is bright
red. Legs are black. Female is
a washed out brown above
with darker ear coverts, pale
throat and breast with orangey
flanks and underside. Juvenile is
similar to female but more gray
and lacks any color on the flanks.

VOICE: A
shrill *whip-
whip-wheril*
repeated
several times.

BEHAVIOR: Like
many flycatchers will
sit close to the edge of a
tree and then fly out
almost hovering in mid
air as it attempts to catch
small flying insects.

HABITAT: Open scrub and
tree-lined waterways.

DISTRIBUTION: Found in Mexico
year round, moving into Texas
and across to Arizona to breed.
A small number winter in southeastern Texas.

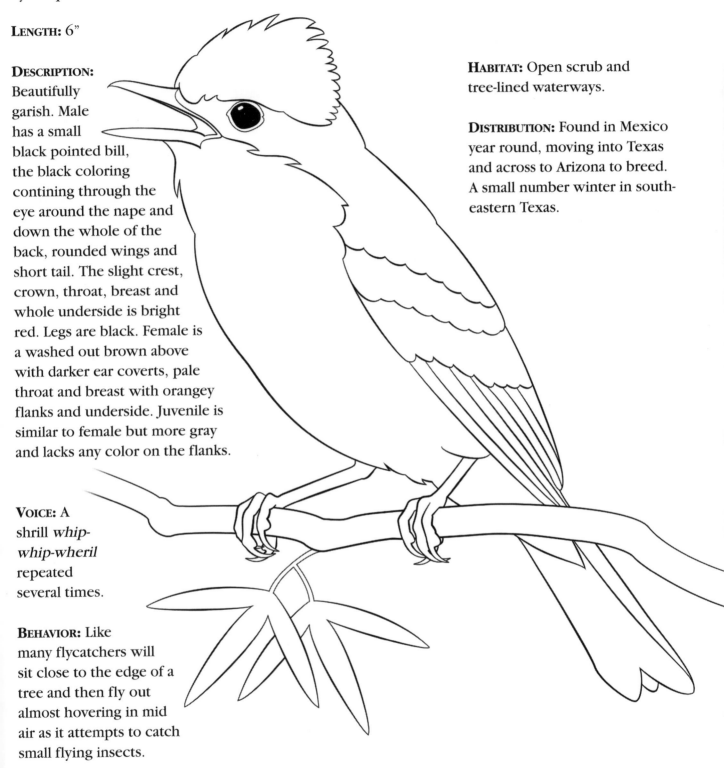

Western Kingbird
Tyrannus verticalis

LENGTH: 8.5"

DESCRIPTION: One of the smaller kingbirds. Adult has a small pointed black bill and a black eye. Head is light gray, throat and breast are pale. Upper breast and underside, including the undertail and underwing, are yellow. Wings are fairly long and are dark brown above (as are the primaries from below). Tail is square and black with white outer edges. Legs are dark. Juvenile is similar to the adult but much paler.

VOICE: A high, squealing *peek-pic-pic-peecabo*.

BEHAVIOR: As happy in towns as it is in the wilds and has adapted well to human habitation. Can be aggressive when nesting and feeding.

HABITAT: Open woodland, parks and suburban gardens.

DISTRIBUTION: Breeds in western states from California as far inland as Minnesota and just into Canada. Some birds winter in southern Florida but most winter in South America.

Yellow-throated Vireo

Vireo flavifrons

LENGTH: 5.5"

DESCRIPTION: A small heavy-headed bird. Small but sturdy dark bill. Black eyes are surrounded by yellow eye rings split by a dark smudge leading down to the bill. The rest of the face and throat is bright yellow, crown and back are a yellowy-green, lower back and rump are gray. Wings are quite long and tail is short, both are gray-black with two white wing-bars and some white edging to the flight feathers. Underside is white and legs are gray.

VOICE: A two part call of *weeoo-weooe* with a pause between each note.

BEHAVIOR: A typical woodland species. Can be found searching for food up in the tree canopy but also in lower bushes. Will often sit out in the open.

HABITAT: Most types of woodland.

DISTRIBUTION: Found in summer from North Dakota south to Louisiana and east to New Hampshire. Winters in South America.

Blue Jay
Cyanocitta cristata

LENGTH: 11"

DESCRIPTION: Adult has a black bill and predominantly white cheeks and throat. A black band goes from the base of the bill through the eye and around the head and breast. Undersides are dirty white-gray becoming more white down the back. Crown (often held up in a crest), nape, back, wings and tail are blue. Wings and tail are barred black. Wings have some white patches and the tail has white tips. Legs are dark. Juvenile is quite similar but paler.

VOICE: Is known to expertly mimic other species but often calls its name, *jaay-jaay*.

BEHAVIOR: A sociable bird and often quite confiding. Can be seen in small flocks searching for its favored food, the acorn. A very vocal bird, groups can be quite noisy.

HABITAT: Open woodland and parks.

DISTRIBUTION: A fairly common resident from eastern Texas to Newfoundland and northwest to Alberta. Rarely seen elsewhere.

143

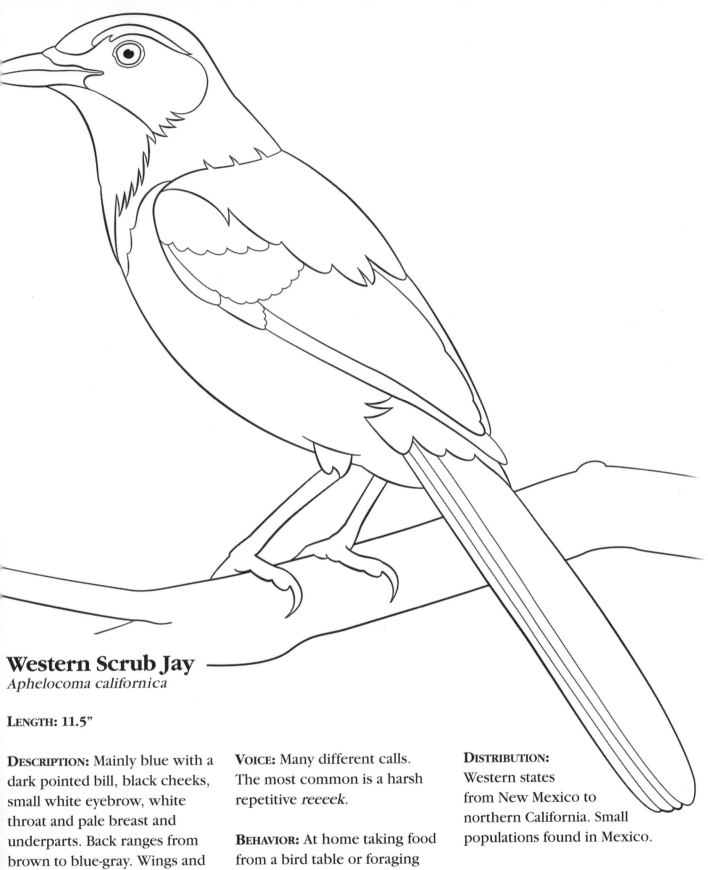

Western Scrub Jay

Aphelocoma californica

LENGTH: 11.5"

DESCRIPTION: Mainly blue with a dark pointed bill, black cheeks, small white eyebrow, white throat and pale breast and underparts. Back ranges from brown to blue-gray. Wings and tail are plain blue with darker tips. Legs are black. Juvenile is much duller, retaining blue wings and tail but slate gray above, slightly lighter below.

VOICE: Many different calls. The most common is a harsh repetitive *reeeek*.

BEHAVIOR: At home taking food from a bird table or foraging amongst leaf litter.

HABITAT: Mature woodland and suburban gardens.

DISTRIBUTION: Western states from New Mexico to northern California. Small populations found in Mexico.

145

Black-billed Magpie
Pica hudsonia

LENGTH: 19"

DESCRIPTION: Large, long-tailed and at first glance black and white. The adult has a heavy black bill and glossy black head, throat, bib, back and undertail. Breast and scapulars are white. Legs are black. Large white patches of the upper and lower primaries are visible in flight. Although the wing and tail appear black they are an iridescent deep blue-green. Tail has a purple tip. Juvenile is not as glossy and has a shorter tail.

VOICE: A loud and harsh *wek-wek-wek-wek*, usually made whilst perched on top or trees or in flight.

BEHAVIOR: Always visible and vocal, very aggressive and often seen harassing smaller birds in gardens for scraps of food. Will often take young nestlings.

HABITAT: Suburban gardens, town parks and scrubland.

DISTRIBUTION: Found from Colorado northwest through western Canada to the Aleutian Islands. A small wintering population is also found in Minnesota.

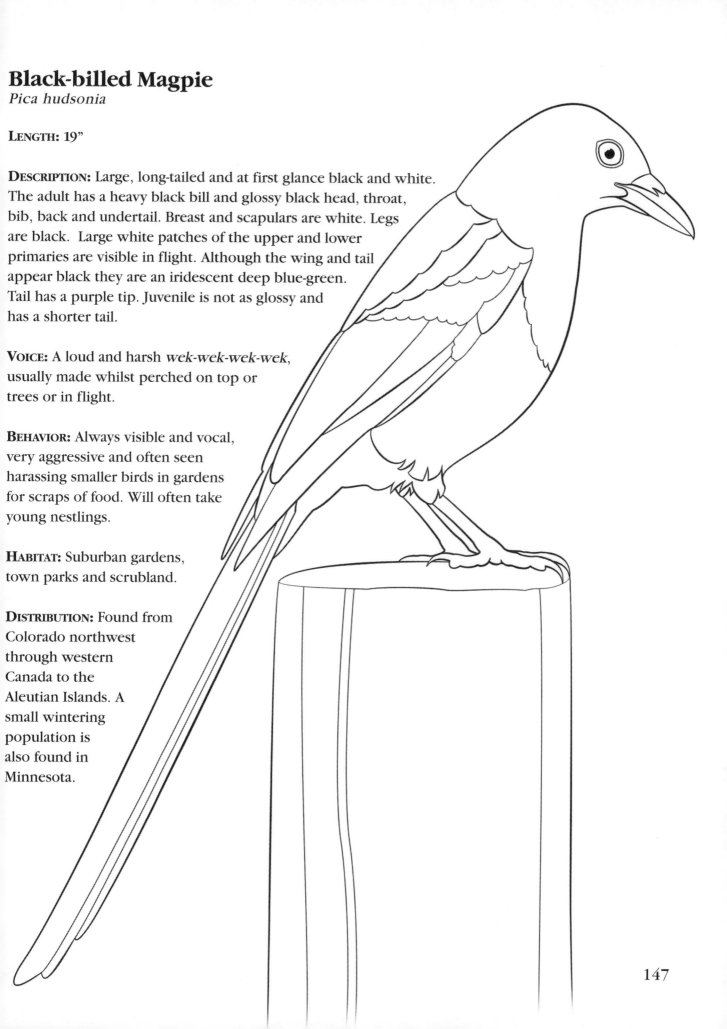

147

Clark's Nutcracker
Nucifraga columbiana

LENGTH: 12"

DESCRIPTION: Who would have thought gray and black could look so appealing? Adult has a black, pointed, slightly down-curved bill, black eyes with white eye-rings and a pale chin. The rest of the head, back, throat, breast and underside is light gray. Wings and tail are mostly black with white-tipped secondaries and white outer-tail feathers most clearly seen in flight. Undertail is white. Legs are gray-black. Juvenile is much like the adult but lacks the white face markings and is browner.

VOICE: A loud abrasive *raa-raa-raa-rak*, which can be heard from some distance.

BEHAVIOR: Often seen high in the tops of pine trees. When seen in flight it is often quite high. Will feed on the forest floor if cones have dropped.

HABITAT: Mature pine forest.

DISTRIBUTION: Resident from Nevada inland to Wyoming then further north to British Columbia.

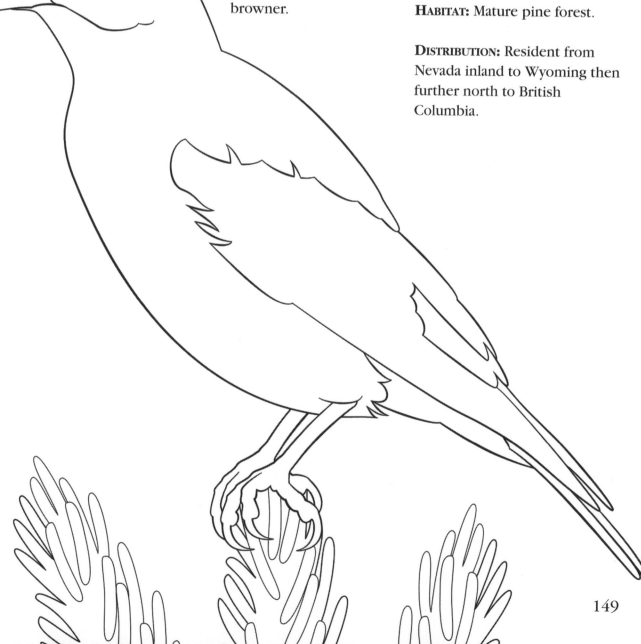

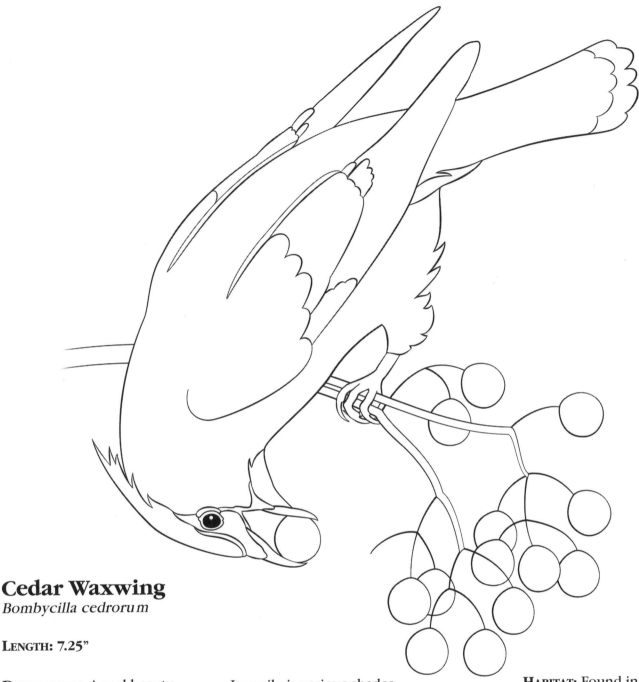

Cedar Waxwing
Bombycilla cedrorum

LENGTH: 7.25"

DESCRIPTION: A real beauty. Striking adult has a white-edged black eye stripe, dark throat and bill standing out against a rich orange-brown crested head. The brown coloring darkens down the back, throat and breast, becoming a buff-yellow. Under-tail is off-white, rump is gray and tail is gray with a yellow tip. The wings are two-toned brown and black with red waxy tips to the secondaries. Legs are black.

Juvenile is various shades of brown, paler underneath, with minimal crest and smaller black facemask with a whiter surround.

VOICE: A high pitched shrill repeated *pseee*.

BEHAVIOR: Will gather in large flocks during the winter months to strip trees and bushes of their berries.

HABITAT: Found in orchards, suburban gardens and woodlands.

DISTRIBUTION: Resident in a swath across the United States from Connecticut to Washington. Winters in all states and south to Mexico. Breeding populations can be seen as far north as the Northwest Territories.

151

Black-capped Chickadee
Pa rus atricapillus

LENGTH: 5.25"

DESCRIPTION: Several races found across the United States are all variations of the same colors, with a small pointed black bill and black eye. Black crown and throat are split by a white cheek stripe that widens towards the nape. Gray-green above with white outer flight feathers. Underside pale to warm buff with white breast. Tail is long for the bird's size. Legs are gray.

VOICE: A clear high pitched two-note *see-mee*.

BEHAVIOR: A sociable little bird, and regular at garden bird tables. Can become incredibly tame. Also found in mixed winter flocks with other small woodland birds in search of food.

HABITAT: Open woodland, parks and suburban gardens.

DISTRIBUTION: Resident from Tennessee westward to Oregon, north to Alaska and northeast to Newfoundland. Rarely seen outside their usual range.

153

Tufted Titmouse

Pa rus bicolor

LENGTH: 9.75"

DESCRIPTION: Two races differ in their head patterns. Both have a tiny black bill and black eye with a white eye patch leading down to the bill. The Northern race has a black forehead and pale gray tuft, while the less common Mexican race has a white forehead and black tuft. Both have a pale gray nape, slightly darker back and tail, white breast and underside and orangey flanks. Juveniles of both races look similar but lack black on the head.

VOICE: A clear and repetitive *peter-peter-peter.*

BEHAVIOR: Energetic and forever on the move. Happy dangling up high in the canopy where they move from branch to branch in search of food. Will also visit garden bird feeders for an easy meal.

HABITAT: Open broadleaved woodland and suburban gardens.

DISTRIBUTION: The Northern race is resident from Minnesota east to New Hampshire and south into Mexico where it overlaps with the Mexican race, which is also found in Texas.

155

Verdin
Auriparus flaviceps

LENGTH: 4.5"

DESCRIPTION: Male has bright yellow head and throat, black eye and bill with a small dark lore patch. Breast and underside are pale. The nape to the tip of the short round tail is shades of gray, darkest on the primaries and tail. The wing has a red shoulder patch. Legs are gray. Female is duller than the male with a little less yellow on the throat. Juvenile is mainly gray above with a hint of yellowy-green coming through, and pale below.

VOICE: A loud and high single *chew*, also repeated several times in a row, *chew-chew-chew*.

BEHAVIOR: Always on the go and quite vocal, making it easy to find if you are in the right place. Does not congregate in large flocks, preferring a more solitary life.

HABITAT: Arid scrub.

DISTRIBUTION: A trip to the south-west is needed if you wish to see this resident species, found from the southern Mojave Desert to Texas and south to Mexico.

Purple Martin
Progne subis

LENGTH: 8"

DESCRIPTION: The largest and darkest swallow found in North America. Male has glossy blue-black head, back, throat and underside. Long pointed wings, tail, bill and legs are black in both male and female. Female has less glossy dark blue crown and back, with gray on the head and breast and dirty off-white underside. Juvenile lacks any blue and looks more like the female, mainly gray above with a pale underside.

VOICE: Most common call is a tuneful *churr-churr-chur-chur.* Also makes a variety of harsher calls.

BEHAVIOR: This backyard favorite will often nest in special martin boxes; otherwise nests in trees. Hawks insects on the wing over land and water.

HABITAT: Rural backyards, parks and open woodland.

DISTRIBUTION: A summer visitor found mainly east of Kansas, although small colonies are present along the west coast and in southern Canada. Winters in South America.

Barn Swallow
Hirundo rustica

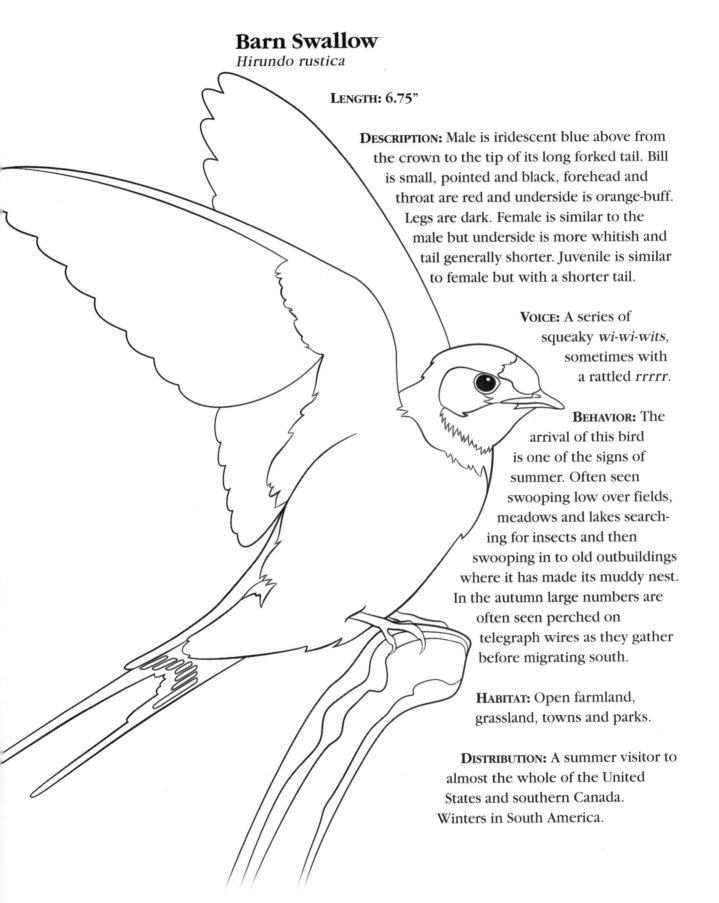

LENGTH: 6.75"

DESCRIPTION: Male is iridescent blue above from the crown to the tip of its long forked tail. Bill is small, pointed and black, forehead and throat are red and underside is orange-buff. Legs are dark. Female is similar to the male but underside is more whitish and tail generally shorter. Juvenile is similar to female but with a shorter tail.

VOICE: A series of squeaky *wi-wi-wits*, sometimes with a rattled *rrrrr*.

BEHAVIOR: The arrival of this bird is one of the signs of summer. Often seen swooping low over fields, meadows and lakes searching for insects and then swooping in to old outbuildings where it has made its muddy nest. In the autumn large numbers are often seen perched on telegraph wires as they gather before migrating south.

HABITAT: Open farmland, grassland, towns and parks.

DISTRIBUTION: A summer visitor to almost the whole of the United States and southern Canada. Winters in South America.

Cliff Swallow
Petrochelidon pyrrhonota

LENGTH: 5.5"

DESCRIPTION: A small, short-tailed swallow. Adult has small round head with black bill and eyes, white forehead and red cheek patches that almost meet below the bill. A light gray collar goes from the nape around to the breast, which becomes paler ranging from off-white to a warm buff at the flanks and rump. Crown and back have a blue tinge but wings are darker above with a pale underside and are rounded compared to other swallows. Legs are light gray. Juvenile is similar to adult but duller around the face with pale underparts.

VOICE: A drawn-out soft *churr*, which can be rather loud when a whole colony calls together.

BEHAVIOR: This social bird is happiest in large groups. Often seen gathering mud to build a round nest with a small entrance tunnel.

HABITAT: From town buildings to gorges; anywhere suitable for siting a nest.

DISTRIBUTION: A summer visitor to most of Canada and the United States. Breeds in most areas except for the southeastern states from North Carolina to Louisiana where it is mainly seen on migration.

Horned Lark
Eremophila alpestris

LENGTH: 7.25"

DESCRIPTION: A long-winged lark. Coloring is very variable but all populations have small, dark pointed bills, black eyes, lores, auriculars, breast band, crown stripe and "horns". Wings and tail center are brown. Tail has black outer feathers with pale edges. Throat, cheeks and supercilium range from white to bright yellow. Nape, shoulders, back, rump and flanks range from pale brown to a rich rufous color. Underside is pale. Some birds show faint barring and yellow coloration. Female has duller face and breast, pale yellow throat and supercilium, pale brown upperparts and pale underparts. Juvenile lacks color and is mottled gray-brown above with grayish underparts.

VOICE: A light *suee-weet* call and also a twittering *tri-it-eet-itit*.

BEHAVIOR: Feeds on dry open ground. Will burst into the air if disturbed and circle around before landing, usually close to the same position. In winter can be found in large flocks, which may include other species such as buntings.

HABITAT: Low dry grassland and tundra.

DISTRIBUTION: Resident except from Mississippi to North Carolina where only wintering birds are seen. Moves north in summer and breeds in much of Canada, reaching as far north as the Queen Elizabeth Islands.

Golden-crowned Kinglet
Regulus satrapa

LENGTH: 4"

DESCRIPTION: A tiny bird. Male has a striking head with small dark bill, and white supercilium separated from a bright yellow and orange crown by a black stripe. Back and tail are olive green. Wings have a yellowish tinge with a white wing-bar and black patches on the upper-wing. Cheeks and flanks are pale gray and the underside paler still. Legs dark but feet pale. Female is similar to the male but lacks the orange at the center of the crown and has just a bright golden yellow stripe. Juvenile is slightly duller and has light gray crown.

VOICE: A series of high-pitched *psee-psee-psee* calls which descend into a rapid *psee-si-si-si*.

BEHAVIOR: Full of energy and always on the move, flitting from one tree to another looking for tiny insects.

HABITAT: Mixed and coniferous woodland.

DISTRIBUTION: Small resident populations are found in the west from Utah north to Alaska and in the east from West Virginia to Newfoundland. Wintering birds are found between these two areas. Breeding birds are also found in southern Canada from the Yukon Territory to the Torngat Mountains.

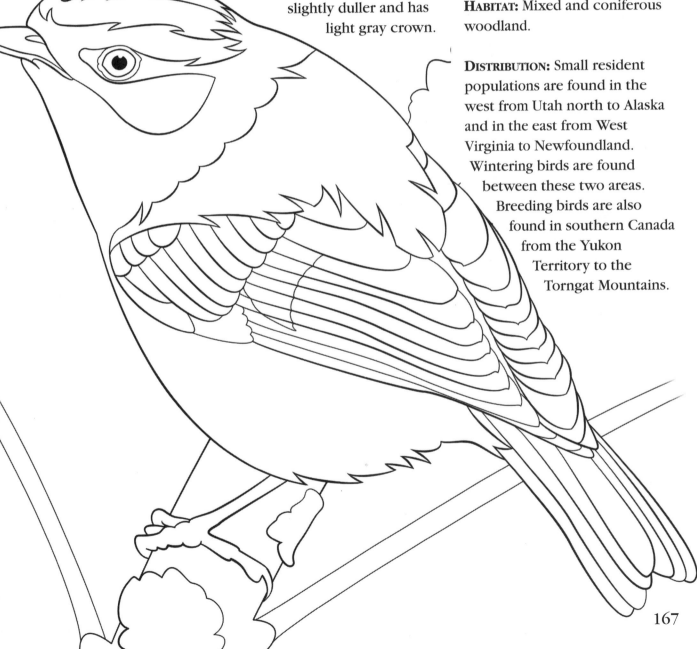

House Wren
Troglodytes aedon

LENGTH: 4.75"

DESCRIPTION: A common bird with plumage varying by area. Body color ranges from gray-brown to a rich warm chestnut brown. Adults of all races have black barring on the wings, under-tail and tail. Tail is quite long and often held upright in the typical wren pose. Main body is quite plain but some races show barring towards the flanks. All races have a pale eye ring around a black eye. Pointed bill is dark above but pale below. Throat varies from off-white to buff. Juvenile is similar to the adult, with coloration ranging from a dull gray-brown to rufous depending on the race.

VOICE: A loud and scratchy series of notes including an angry *churr*.

BEHAVIOR: Moves around low bushes and ground cover in search of small insects. Inconspicuous until it bursts into song, which for a small bird is incredibly loud.

HABITAT: Open woodland, parks, hedgerows and gardens.

DISTRIBUTION: Breeds over most of the United States north of a line from California to Tennessee and into southern Canada. Winters south of this line.

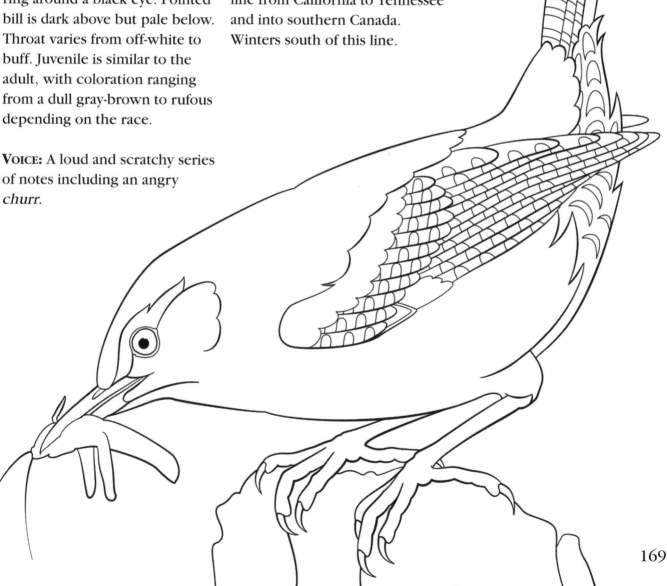

Blue-gray Gnatcatcher
Polioptila caerulea

LENGTH: 4.5"

DESCRIPTION: A small common bird. Summer adult is a warm blue-gray above with darker primaries and a long dark tail with white outer feathers. Underside from the throat to tail is paler. Bill is small, dark and pointed. A black forehead stripe extends to the eye, which is black with a pale eye-ring. The amount of black and overall brightness of the bird depends on race. Legs are dark gray. Winter adult and juvenile duller and often browner but all retain the obvious eye-ring.

VOICE: A jumbled mess of high-pitched *swee*, *spee* and *szweep* calls.

BEHAVIOR: Likes to forage in bushes and trees, often quite high in the canopy. Always on the move, flitting from one branch to another using its tail as a tool to move leaves as it searches for small insects.

HABITAT: Woodland and bushy scrub.

DISTRIBUTION: Resident from Texas to South Carolina. Summer range extends north as far as Wisconsin in the east and Idaho in the west.

Red-breasted Nuthatch
Sitta canadensis •

LENGTH: 4.5"

DESCRIPTION: Male has a small slightly upturned and pointed black bill, black crown and eye stripe and white supercilium and cheeks The short rounded wings and tail are a rich blue and the throat, breast and underside are red. Tail is short with pale underfeathers. Legs are gray. Female is paler than the male with more white around the face and throat and a softer pale orange belly.

VOICE: A clear nasally *yaank-yaank-yaank*.

BEHAVIOR: Creeps close to the tree trunk or branch when feeding, but will sit upright when not feeding. In late autumn and winter may be found in mixed flocks with other small woodland birds and will also visit garden birdfeeders.

HABITAT: Mainly woodland but will visit gardens.

DISTRIBUTION: Resident in most of southern Canada from Quebec to the Yukon Territory and in some western states of the United States south to New Mexico. Wintering birds are found across North America apart from the tip of Florida.

White-breasted Nuthatch
Sitta carolinensis

LENGTH: 5.75"

DESCRIPTION: A large nuthatch with a long upturned bill. Slight variations in plumage and shape depend on location. A black crown stripe ends in a semi-collar at the base of the nape. Back is blue-gray, with some black and white feathering on the wing and tail. Face and underside are white becoming grayer further down the breast and flanks. Rear flanks and undertail are reddish orange. Legs are pale gray. Female is similar to male but colors are not as bold.

VOICE: A series of *haa-haa-haa-haa* calls. Pitch and speed differ depending on region.

BEHAVIOR: Similar to their Red-breasted cousins in the way they feed, they are happy hanging upside down beneath branches. Will also visit birdfeeders, where their bigger size is obvious.

HABITAT: Usually found in mature woodland but also visits garden feeders.

DISTRIBUTION: Resident in a broad swath from California to Maine and southern Canada.

Brown Creeper
Certhia americana

LENGTH: 5.25"

DESCRIPTION: An expert in blending in to its surroundings. Adult has a long down-curved bill and white supercilium. Upperside is mottled brown-gray and white from the base of the bill to the tip of the long stiff tail. The rump and tail can appear a more uniform lighter brown. Underside is pale off-white becoming buff towards the flanks. Legs are pale. Juvenile is duller than the adult with some barring on the underside.

VOICE: A single high pitched *pseee* and a fluty *psee-seeado-psee-oby*.

BEHAVIOR: As its name suggests, this bird likes to creep around trees. Expert at climbing up and down trunks, it uses its thin bill to probe the bark looking for grubs.

HABITAT: Mature woodland.

DISTRIBUTION: Resident in west coast states from New Mexico to British Columbia, across southern Canada to Quebec and into the eastern states down to New York. Winters across most of the United States and southern Canada.

177

Gray Catbird
Dumetella carolinensis

LENGTH: 8.5"

DESCRIPTION: Very distinctive. Adult has a sturdy, pointed black bill. Crown, tail and legs are black. Undertail coverts are rufous; the rest of the bird is uniform slate gray. Juvenile is similar but slightly paler.

VOICE: A rambled confusion of sound including *tsiiih, chak-kak-kak* and a distinctive *mew*. Song can be quite slow at times, sometimes speeding up before returning to a controlled pace.

BEHAVIOR: Rarely seen flying across open ground, preferring to hide in dense vegetation. When perched on a branch will often pose with tail up and wings down as if ready to run off.

HABITAT: Dense scrub, thickets and young stands of woodland.

DISTRIBUTION: A modest resident population is found along the east coast from Georgia to New Jersey. Summer range spreads west to Idaho and north to Alberta. Wintering birds are found from Florida south to Mexico.

179

Brown Thrasher
Toxostoma rufum

LENGTH: 11.5"

DESCRIPTION: A large thrush-like bird. Adult has a medium-sized dark bill, a gray face and yellow eyes. Throat, underside, underwing and undertail coverts are pale to buff with dark streaking. Upperside from the crown to the tip of the long fan-like tail is richly rufous. Wings show two black-edged white wing bars. Legs are pale. Juvenile is similar but not as bright above and eyes are gray.

VOICE: A jumble of *psee-chee, peterwo-peterwo, ch-ch-ch* and a clear *psack.*

BEHAVIOR: Hops around leaf litter looking for caterpillars and other insects. Prefers the shelter of dense vegetation and often disappears suddenly.

HABITAT: Found in dense scrub, thickets and hedgerows.

DISTRIBUTION: Resident from eastern Texas to Virginia. Moves north and west in summer to reach Montana and southern Canada. Some wintering birds move south as far as western Texas and New Mexico.

Varied Thrush
Ixoreus naevius

LENGTH: 9.5"

DESCRIPTION: An appealing patchwork of black and orange. Male has an orange supercilium, throat, breast, flanks and wing-bars, with a black crown, eye-stripe, breast-band, wings and tail. Back, rump and upper flanks are gray. Under-belly and undertail coverts are off-white and legs are pale. Female is much duller except for the wings; the other strong black markings are replaced by gray and the orange is washed out. Juvenile is duller still and much browner overall.

VOICE: High drawn out *pseeeeeep-pseeeeeep,* a shorter *chup-pseeep* and a single *zreet.*

BEHAVIOR: Forages on dark and damp forest floors. In winter will gather with other birds in fair-sized flocks.

HABITAT: Found mainly in damp, mature coniferous forests.

DISTRIBUTION: Rare in eastern and central United States. Small resident populations in Oregon and Washington. In summer spreads northwest to northern Alaska. A small number of wintering birds move south to California and northern Mexico.

Western Bluebird

Sialia mexicana

LENGTH: 7"

DESCRIPTION: An outstandingly beautiful bird. The male's head, throat, back, wings and tail are all bright blue. Breast and shoulders are red, underside and underwing are pale blue-gray. The small pointed bill, eyes and legs are all black. Female has some bright blue on the outer wing and tail but head is gray-blue and the throat is grayer still. Breast is paler red and back is brown-gray. Juvenile has some blue in the wings and tail but is much browner overall with pale flecking above and a pale eye-ring.

VOICE: A chattering burst of song, *few-few-ffew*.

BEHAVIOR: Often sits on bushes, on telegraph wires or in trees, looking for small insects.

HABITAT: Open woodland and parks.

DISTRIBUTION: Found mainly on the west coast from Washington to Mexico. Summering birds push the range a little further north to British Columbia. A small number of wintering birds are found in Texas.

Wood Thrush
Hylocichla mustelina

LENGTH: 7.75"

DESCRIPTION: A medium-sized thrush with an upright stance. Adult has a white eye-ring, and white throat, breast, underside and undertail covered in black spots. Cheeks are black with some pale flecking. Crown, nape, back and tail are chestnut, slightly brighter on the head. Primaries and secondaries are darker brown and the underwing is pale buff. Legs are pink. Juvenile is similar but face is paler and plumage more streaky overall.

VOICE: A fluty *wrr-weo-weo-cchrrr* and a loud quick *whit-whit-whit-whit*.

BEHAVIOR: Forages on woodland floor in search of insects but usually sings from a prominent branch. Often heard before seen.

HABITAT: Prefers the cover of large mature woodland.

DISTRIBUTION: Winters in South America but is a regular summer visitor to the central and eastern United States from Texas north to Minnesota and eastwards to Nova Scotia.

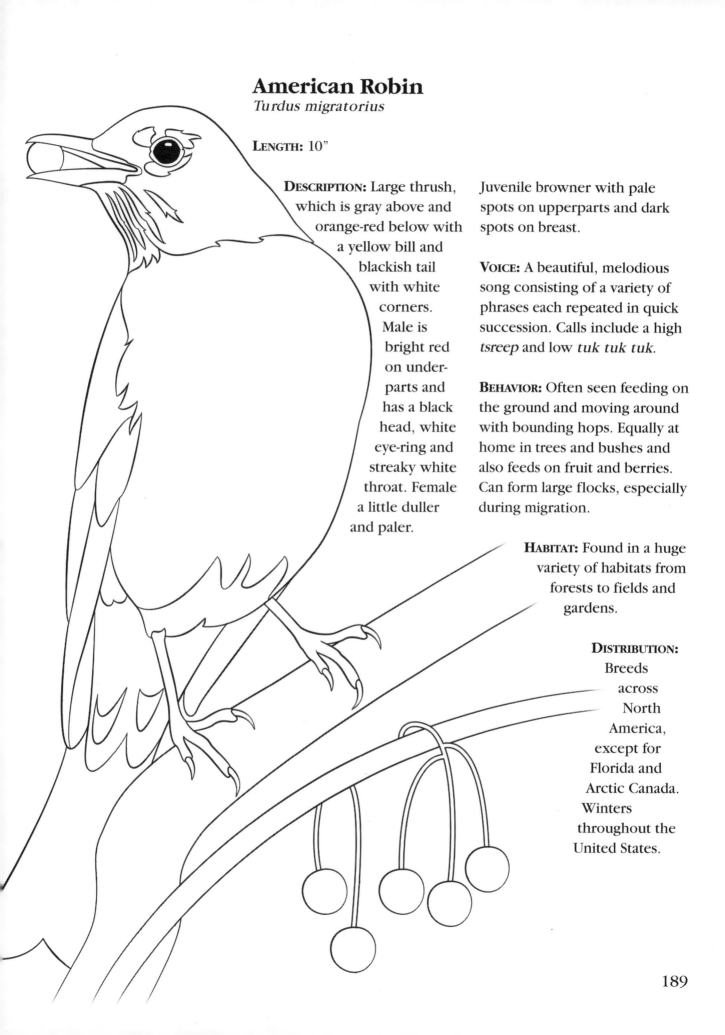

American Robin
Turdus migratorius

LENGTH: 10"

DESCRIPTION: Large thrush, which is gray above and orange-red below with a yellow bill and blackish tail with white corners. Male is bright red on underparts and has a black head, white eye-ring and streaky white throat. Female a little duller and paler.

Juvenile browner with pale spots on upperparts and dark spots on breast.

VOICE: A beautiful, melodious song consisting of a variety of phrases each repeated in quick succession. Calls include a high *tsreep* and low *tuk tuk tuk.*

BEHAVIOR: Often seen feeding on the ground and moving around with bounding hops. Equally at home in trees and bushes and also feeds on fruit and berries. Can form large flocks, especially during migration.

HABITAT: Found in a huge variety of habitats from forests to fields and gardens.

DISTRIBUTION: Breeds across North America, except for Florida and Arctic Canada. Winters throughout the United States.

189

American Goldfinch
Carduelis tristis

LENGTH: 5"

DESCRIPTION: Summer male has a pale, heavy, pointed bill. Forehead and tail are black. Wings are black with white wing-bars. The rest of the head and body is bright yellow, except for the rump and undersides, which are white. Legs are pink. Winter male is a fawny color with a yellow tinge to the throat. Summer female has similar markings to the male but is duller and the body is pale yellow. Winter female is light brown above and pale below and may show a little yellow at times around the throat.

VOICE: A high pitched and fast series of *shwee-shwee* and a series of chattering short *chi chi* calls.

BEHAVIOR: Regularly visits garden feeders and often seen in large flocks feeding on seeds at the edges of fields.

HABITAT: Open farmland, field boundaries and gardens.

DISTRIBUTION: Resident across much of the United States. Summering birds are found in southern Canada. Winters as far south as Mexico.

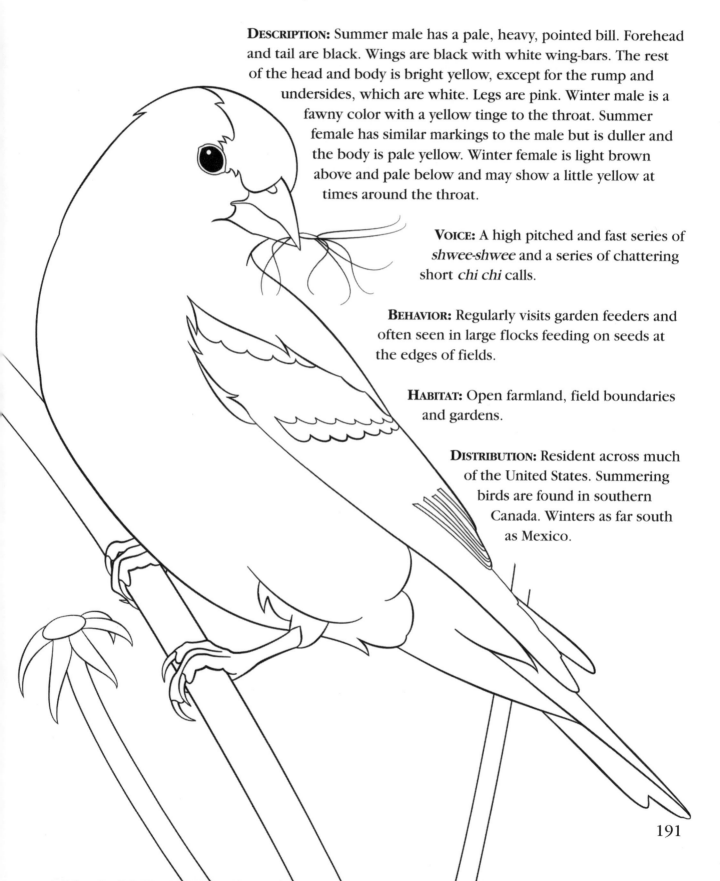

House Finch
Carpodacus mexicanus

LENGTH: 6"

DESCRIPTION: A mid-sized finch with a short pale bill. Male has a red crown, malar, breast and rump. Cheeks and wings are brown-gray; belly and flanks are pale with heavy light brown streaking. Female is brown-gray above and pale with heavy streaks below.

Juvenile looks similar to female but head is streaked. Legs and eyes black in all forms.

VOICE: A drawn out warble of short notes which tail off towards the end.

BEHAVIOR: A communal bird that happily gathers at garden bird-feeders. Feeds on fallen seeds at the edge of fields but is also found in open woodland.

HABITAT: Gardens, field edges and open woodland.

DISTRIBUTION: Resident throughout the United States except southern Florida.

Evening Grosbeak

Hesperiphona vespertina

LENGTH: 8"

DESCRIPTION: A thickset grosbeak with a large triangular pale bill. Male has a yellow supercilium, back, breast and underside, head, throat and neck are chocolate brown, eyes, tail and wings are black except for a large white wing patch. Legs are pink. Female only has yellow on the nape, head is gray as is the back, wings and tail are black and white, throat is pale, breast and flanks pale buff and undertail is white. Juvenile is similar to female but will still have large wing patch if it is male.

VOICE: A loud harsh *churrp*

BEHAVIOR: A gregarious bird often found in large noisy flock perched in trees, will also visit gardens.

HABITAT: Field edges, farmland and suburban gardens

DISTRIBUTION: Resident from New Mexico to Colorado and then from California to British Columbia and across southern Canada to Newfoundland. Winters throughout much of the United States, as far south as east Texas.

195

Yellow Warbler
Dendroica petechia

LENGTH: 5"

DESCRIPTION: A small but stout warbler. Male has bright yellow head, underparts and wing-bars. Underparts finely streaked red on breast and flanks. Nape, mantle, wings, rump and tail are bright greenish-yellow. Bill and eye are dark. Legs are pink.

Female is plainer and slightly duller, with more green on the head and lacking red streaking underneath. Juvenile is plain brownish-yellow.

VOICE: Sings a lively *weet weet wi wi wi too too*, calls a high *tsip*.

BEHAVIOR: Constantly on the move. Feeds on insects, usually in trees. Despite its bright colors it can be surprisingly difficult to see among leaves.

HABITAT: Woodlands, marshes and other habitats with trees and bushes.

DISTRIBUTION: Common summer visitor to most of North America. Winters in Central and South America.

Cape May Warbler

Dendroica tigrina

LENGTH: 5"

DESCRIPTION: Small and bright. Male has a small pointed black bill, bright yellow supercilium, lower cheeks, throat and rump. Breast is yellow with black streaking. A red-orange patch surrounds the eye. Upperparts are green-brown with white patches on the wings and tail. During winter colors fade. Female lacks the red facial markings and the yellow is not as bright. Head and back appear grayer and although some white is seen in the wings it is not as obvious as in the male. Juvenile lacks yellow on head and front and has a greener appearance overall.

VOICE: A high repeated *psip*.

BEHAVIOR: Feeds on insects, especially spruce bud-worms.

HABITAT: Most often seen in spruce woodland.

DISTRIBUTION: A summer migrant, breeding mainly in Canada from the Northwest Territories east to Maine. Migrates north and east from Florida. Winters in Central America.

Yellow-rumped Warbler
Dendroica coronata

LENGTH: 5.5"

DESCRIPTION: A relatively large, colorful warbler. Male has a yellow crown stripe, throat, rump and flanks. Eye-ring, undertail and undersides are white. Undersides and breast have heavy black markings, upperparts are slate gray with black flecks and white bars in the wings and tail. Some races have less black on the body and a white throat. Female lacks crown stripe and is paler gray with less defined streaking and less white in the wings. Juvenile tends to be brown and streaky. Bill, legs and eyes black in all forms.

VOICE: Calls *swee-swee-si-si-swee;* pitch varies depending on race.

BEHAVIOR: Acts like a flycatcher and is often found flying up from a perch to catch insects. When at rest often has its yellow rump on display.

HABITAT: Open woodland, parks and bushy open spaces.

DISTRIBUTION: Breeds from Arizona to Alaska and east to Labrador. Small resident populations are found on the west coast. Winters in southern states and Mexico.

Townsend's Warbler
Dendroica townsendi

LENGTH: 5"

DESCRIPTION: A mid-sized wood warbler. Male's crown, cheeks, throat and flanks are black and the breast, supercilium, malar and a small eye patch are yellow. Wings and tail are dark with white wing bars and outer tail feathers. Back and rump are greenish and underside is white. Female has yellow markings but crown, cheeks, throat and flanks are greenish rather than black. Throat is pale yellow with black edging and some dark streaking. Juvenile much like female.

VOICE: A number of scratchy notes which change in pitch towards the end *zee-ze-ze-zeeee-di-di-dee.*

BEHAVIOR: Spends most of its time amongst foliage in search of small insects and bugs.

HABITAT: Mature coniferous forests.

DISTRIBUTION: Mainly a summer visitor breeding from Idaho to Alaska. Migratory birds are found in the western states as far south as New Mexico. Some winter along the coast of Oregon and California.

Black-and-white Warbler

Mniotila varia

LENGTH: 5"

DESCRIPTION: An unmistakable 'flying candy'. Male has longish dark bill and legs, black and white striped head with a large white crown stripe and supercilium and a white eye-ring clearly visible against a black eye-stripe. Heavily streaked below. Two white wingbars stand out in otherwise black wings. Tail is black. An all-black throat becomes more uneven in winter. Female is paler than the male with a narrower black eye-stripe and a white throat and is less streaked below. Juveniles resemble adults but are much duller.

VOICE: Goes from a soft *tzit* to a hard *tick* if startled when feeding. Song is a repetitive *sue-wee-sue*.

BEHAVIOR: Scales trunks and branches of trees from top to bottom, creeping like a nuthatch to look for insects. May hover to take food from leaves.

HABITAT: Prefers damp woods, but can be found a variety of woodland habitats. Will move to more scrubby areas in winter.

DISTRIBUTION: Summers in northern and eastern North America. Winters from the Gulf coast to the West Indies and south to South America.

American Redstart
Setophaga ruticilla

LENGTH: 5.25"

DESCRIPTION: The unmistakable summer male is jet black with bright orange wing-bars, tail patches and flanks and a white underside. In the female the orange is replaced by yellow, the head and underside are light gray and the back and rump are olive green. Juvenile is similar to female, although if male may have black markings. Legs are black in all forms.

VOICE: A number of high *se-se-seweet* calls and a repeated *pseet*.

BEHAVIOR: Will often sit with tail cocked and fanned out and wings down, displaying its bright colors, then jump around, possibly hoping to startle small bugs to feed on.

HABITAT: Mixed open woodland or broadleaf forests.

DISTRIBUTION: A wide breeding range from Louisiana northeast to Newfoundland and northwest to Canada's Yukon Territory. Migratory birds pass through some western states but are rarely found on the west coast. Small numbers are seen wintering in Florida.

Common Yellowthroat
Geothlypis trichas

LENGTH: 5"

DESCRIPTION: A masked beauty. Male has a black face mask, eye and small pointed bill. The mask is bordered at the top by a light gray stripe. Throat, belly and undertail are all bright yellow. Crown, back, wings and tail are a pale green-buff with a hint of yellow. There are several races across North America and the brightness and extent of color varies. Legs are pink in all cases. Female lacks the black mask and gray border and has a brown-green head, pale yellow throat and pale buff underside. Juvenile is like the female.

VOICE: A high pitched *whipity- whipity- whipty-whip* and a harsh *chat*.

BEHAVIOR: Rather secretive, preferring dense cover.

HABITAT: Dense patches of cover close to water.

DISTRIBUTION: Found in summer over almost all of the United States and much of Canada as far north as Yukon Territory. Resident birds are found from North Carolina to Louisiana.

Yellow-breasted Chat

Icteria virens

LENGTH: 7.5"

DESCRIPTION: A large warbler with a heavy black pointed bill. Adult has a striking yellow throat, breast and underwing. Head is grayish with white markings around the eye and malar and black lores. Back, rump, rounded wings and fan-like tail are greenish-brown. Underside and undertail are white. Juvenile is like adult but front is darker and mottled. Legs are dark in all cases.

VOICE: A harsh *wek-wek-wek* and a more drawn out *whoup-whoup*.

BEHAVIOR: Very secretive. Prefers to stay hidden in bushes.

HABITAT: Usually found in mature woodland.

DISTRIBUTION: A summer visitor across the United States, but not commonly seen around the southern region of the Great Lakes. Some birds cross into Canada around Alberta.

Baltimore Oriole
Icterus galbula

LENGTH: 8.75"

DESCRIPTION: A brightly colored summer visitor. Head, throat, back, some of the tail and most of the wings are black in the male. Breast, belly, rump, tail edges and two shoulder patches are orange. A variable amount of white barring is seen on the wing. Bill and legs are pale gray. Female lacks much of the black coloring, retaining it only on the wings. White wing bars are also retained but the rest of the body ranges from greenish to yellow-orange. Juvenile is similar to female but browner.

VOICE: A whistled *peehew-peehew-peehew-hew-diue.*

BEHAVIOR: Likes tree-lined open spaces. Will visit gardens in search of fruit, with oranges being a particular favorite.

HABITAT: Open woodland, parks and suburban gardens.

DISTRIBUTION: A summer visitor from Oklahoma northeast to Nova Scotia and northwest to Alberta. Migratory birds can be found at the edges of this range. A small population winters around the coast of Florida.

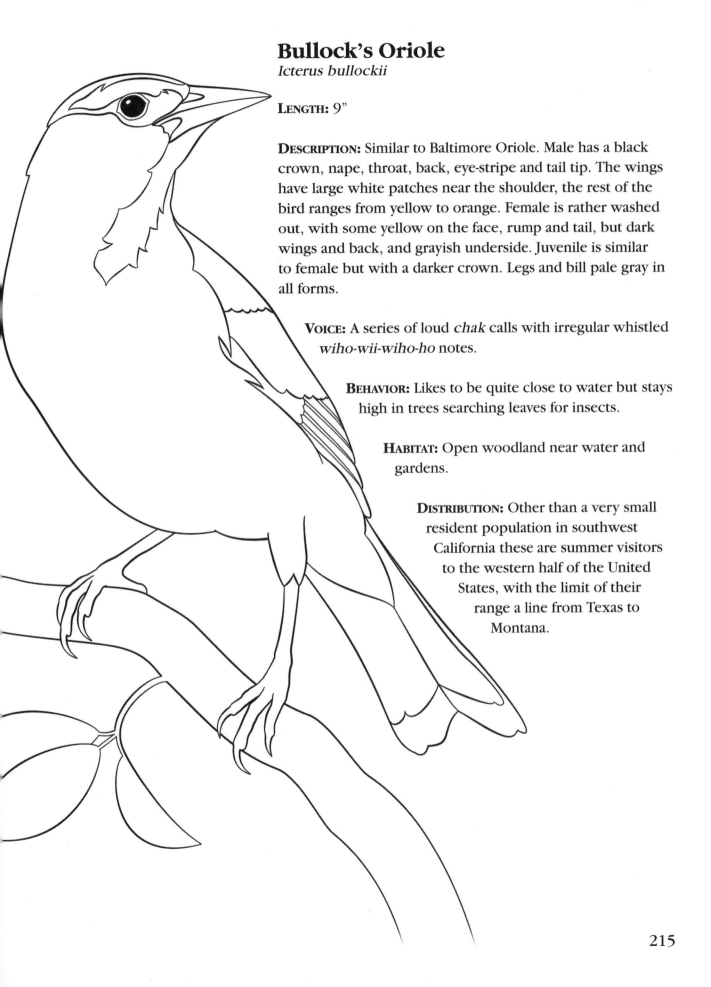

Bullock's Oriole
Icterus bullockii

LENGTH: 9"

DESCRIPTION: Similar to Baltimore Oriole. Male has a black crown, nape, throat, back, eye-stripe and tail tip. The wings have large white patches near the shoulder, the rest of the bird ranges from yellow to orange. Female is rather washed out, with some yellow on the face, rump and tail, but dark wings and back, and grayish underside. Juvenile is similar to female but with a darker crown. Legs and bill pale gray in all forms.

VOICE: A series of loud *chak* calls with irregular whistled *wiho-wii-wiho-ho* notes.

BEHAVIOR: Likes to be quite close to water but stays high in trees searching leaves for insects.

HABITAT: Open woodland near water and gardens.

DISTRIBUTION: Other than a very small resident population in southwest California these are summer visitors to the western half of the United States, with the limit of their range a line from Texas to Montana.

Red-winged Blackbird
Agelaius phoeniceus

LENGTH: 8.75"

DESCRIPTION: A distinctive bird. Male is glossy black all over except for shoulder patches, which are mostly red with some yellow (some races lack the yellow). Female is mottled redbrown and buff, with some warmer orange, especially around the face in some races. Juvenile is like female with a paler underside. Legs and bill are dark in all forms.

VOICE: A loud babbling *hon-kooeee.*

BEHAVIOR: Can be found in almost all open spaces feeding in full view. During the winter months large flocks can form with other species.

HABITAT: Scrub, open woodland parks and gardens.

DISTRIBUTION: Resident across the United States and in summer found across Canada as far north as Great Bear Lake.

Western Meadowlark
Sturnella neglecta

LENGTH: 9.5"

DESCRIPTION: Adult has a large, pointed, pale gray bill, a yellow throat, breast, underside and eye-patch and black breast-band. Cheeks and undertail are gray-buff with black flecking. Black markings are also seen across the light brown upperparts. Underwing is pale gray. Outer tail feathers and supercilium are white. Legs are pale. Juvenile is like the adult but paler.

VOICE: A single harsh *chuk* or a bubbling *wida-bi-di-da-along*.

BEHAVIOR: Often seen singing out in the open in full view on a post or telegraph wire. Feeds mainly on the ground.

HABITAT: Open grassy areas.

DISTRIBUTION: Resident on the west coast from Washington inland to Iowa and south to Mexico. During the breeding season the range expands to southern Canada and east to Michigan.

219

Bobolink
Dolichonyx oryzivorus

Length: 7"

Description: Male unmistakable during the breeding season. Plumage is all black except for a white back, rump and wing patch and a creamy yellow nape. Non-breeding male is completely different: orangey buff with dark streaking and black crown, eye-stripe and tail. Female is like non-breeding male but has a browner back and tail, is lighter on the underside and has a pale crown stripe. Juvenile is like the female but brighter.

Voice: A pleasant array of notes interspersed with a harsh *chuk*.

Behavior: Often found in large flocks outside breeding season. Likes to feed amongst grasses and small bushes of open scrub.

Habitat: Open grassland, scrub and meadows.

Distribution: Summer visitor found in most states north, east and west of Missouri and up to southern Canada. Migrating birds are found southeast to Florida. Winters in South America.

White-crowned Sparrow
Zonotrichia leucophrys

LENGTH: 7"

DESCRIPTION: A sparrow with variant plumage depending on race and location. Adults all have black and white striped heads, with an obvious white crown. Brightness of plumage differs across the range, as does the bill color, which ranges from yellow-orange to pink. Nape, throat and breast are pale gray; flanks, rump and tail are shades of brown. Wings are a richer brown above with two white bars but are gray from below. Juvenile is similar to adult but the head is brown and buff rather than black and white.

VOICE: Varies across the range but all are high pitched and feature *psee* and *zerrr* notes.

BEHAVIOR: Usually found low down in hedges or feeding close to cover on the ground. Will sometimes visit garden feeders but prefers field borders.

HABITAT: Farmland and hedgerows.

DISTRIBUTION: Breeds mainly in Canada, as far north as Nunavut. A resident population is found around Nevada and wintering birds are found from the Great Lakes south to Mexico.

American Tree Sparrow

Spizella arborea

LENGTH: 6.25"

DESCRIPTION: Male has a chestnut crown and small eye-stripe, a small, pointed black and yellow bill and pale gray face. Breast is pale gray with a small black spot in the middle. Underparts are off-white with pale to buff flanks, tail is long and dark and wings are a mixture of rich browns and blacks with two white bars above and pale below. Juvenile is similar to the adult but has prominent streaks. Legs are pale in all forms.

VOICE: A pleasant high-pitched *pseet-pi-pi-di-se-se-sweet.*

BEHAVIOR: Feeds on the ground in rough scrubby areas. Can be seen in flocks in winter, when it is a regular visitor to gardens.

HABITAT: Open scrubland and rocky hillsides.

DISTRIBUTION: Breeds through most of Alaska and northern Canada to the Arctic borders but winters across the United States as far south as Oklahoma. Can be found anywhere in this range during migration.

Eastern Towhee
Pipilo erythrophthalmus

LENGTH: 8.5"

DESCRIPTION: A mid-sized towhee. Male has a gray pointed bill and black head, throat and back. Wing is black with a white bar, tail feathers are black with white tips. Breast is white, undertail is buff and sides and flanks are rufous. Female similar to male but with chocolate brown coloring rather than black. Juvenile has a plain brown head and throat with some pale buff flecking. Undersides are shades of buff and upperparts are dark. Legs pale in all forms.

VOICE: A high and trill *dink-ah-wi-e-e-e-e-e*.

BEHAVIOR: Spends a lot of time scratching around in dense undergrowth and so can be quite hard to see.

HABITAT: Woodland and dense thickets.

DISTRIBUTION: Resident from North Carolina to Mississippi and inland to Missouri. Breeding ranges push further inland to North Dakota and just across the border to Canada. Wintering populations are found in Texas and Mexico.

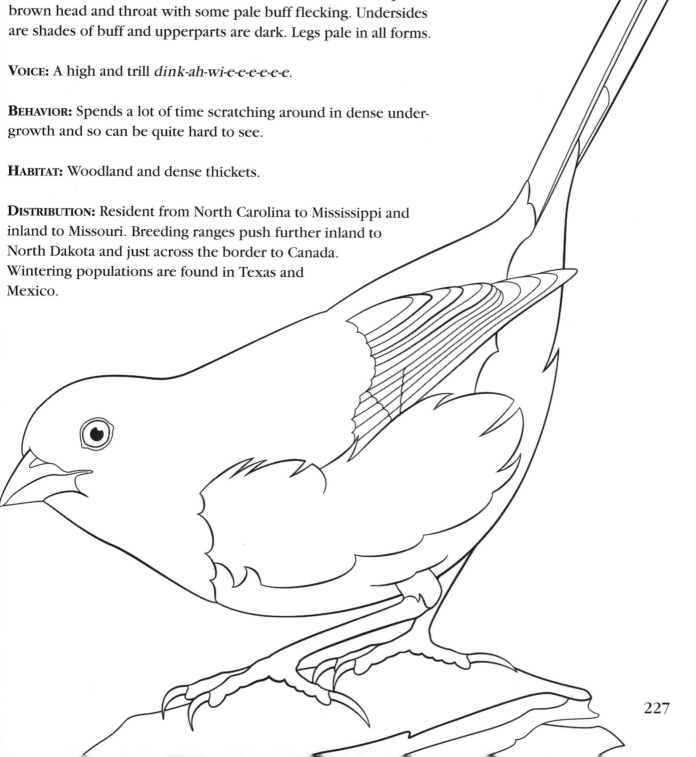

Dickcissel
Spiza americana

LENGTH: 6.25"

DESCRIPTION: Although not in the same family, the Dickcissel is reminiscent of a sparrow. Male has a wedge-shaped gray bill, yellow and white supercilium and malar, a yellow throat and a black bib. The rest of the head, nape and rump are gray, the back is chestnut-black and the tail is dark. The underside is white. Female is a washed out version of the male but lacks the black bib; the crown is dark and supercilium all yellow. Juvenile is a duller version of the female. Legs are pale gray.

VOICE: Call is a dry *chink-chink-chink-sis-sis-sil.*

BEHAVIOR: Feeds on the ground in open grassland. Can form spectacularly large flocks prior to migration.

HABITAT: Grassland and fields.

DISTRIBUTION: A summer migrant found from Texas north to southern Canada and northeast as far as Ohio. Migrating birds can be seen in the southern states. Wintering grounds are in South America.

Black-headed Grosbeak
Pheucticus melanocephalus

LENGTH: 8.25"

DESCRIPTION: A stocky grosbeak. Male has a pale gray bill and black head. Back, wings and tail are black and white with large white patches more visible in flight. Underwing is yellow. Undertail coverts are white and the remainder of the body is bright orange. In winter males become much duller with first year birds showing some buff coloring and a pale supercilium. Female has a dark crown and cheeks split by white eye and chin stripes. The throat is buff-orange, underside is pale and streaked, and the upperside is mostly dark brown with some white.

VOICE: A whistled series of notes including *wheep-we-a-wup*.

BEHAVIOR: Feeds amongst trees and also seen at garden feeders.

HABITAT: Open woodland, parks and gardens.

DISTRIBUTION: Breeds from New Mexico to British Columbia. Rarely seen further east or north. Winters in Mexico.

231

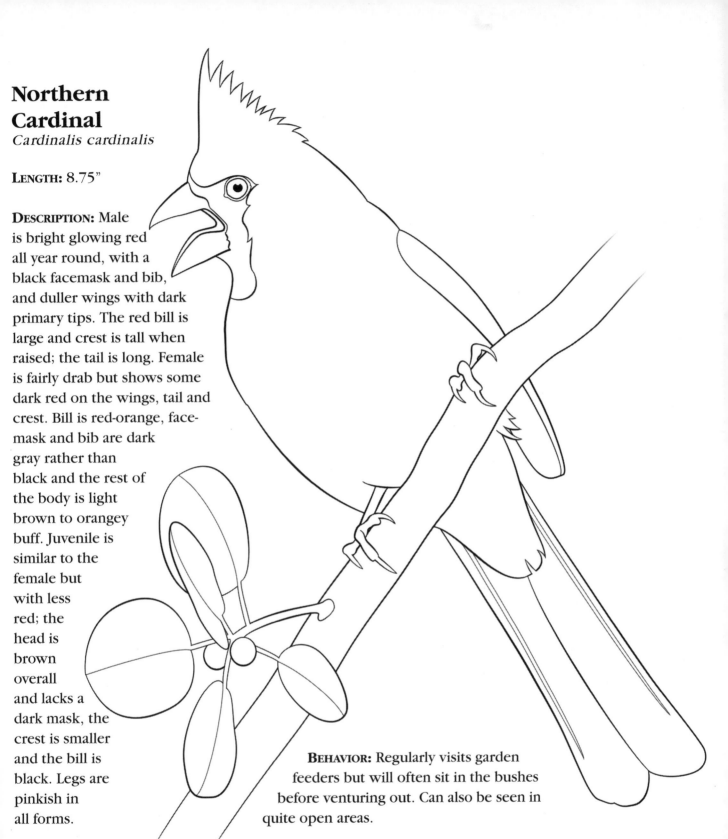

Northern Cardinal
Cardinalis cardinalis

LENGTH: 8.75"

DESCRIPTION: Male is bright glowing red all year round, with a black facemask and bib, and duller wings with dark primary tips. The red bill is large and crest is tall when raised; the tail is long. Female is fairly drab but shows some dark red on the wings, tail and crest. Bill is red-orange, face-mask and bib are dark gray rather than black and the rest of the body is light brown to orangey buff. Juvenile is similar to the female but with less red; the head is brown overall and lacks a dark mask, the crest is smaller and the bill is black. Legs are pinkish in all forms.

VOICE: Many calls, mostly high pitched, including one that sounds like *lookout-lookout-lookout.*

BEHAVIOR: Regularly visits garden feeders but will often sit in the bushes before venturing out. Can also be seen in quite open areas.

HABITAT: Open bushy areas, parks and gardens.

DISTRIBUTION: A common resident found from Texas northeast to Maine and north to South Dakota.

233

Blue Grosbeak
Guiraca caerula

LENGTH: 7"

DESCRIPTION: Small grosbeak with a large bill. Adult male is plain deep blue on head, breast, belly and flanks. Mantle, wings and tail are streaked blue, black and brown. Has a black face-mask and two prominent red-brown wing-bars. Bill and legs bluish-gray. In female the blue is replaced by gray-brown, but usually shows some paler blue on wings and tail; wing-bars pale rufous; bill grayish with pink lower mandible.

VOICE: A rough warbling song. Call a hard *pink*.

BEHAVIOR: Seen in pairs or small groups. Often feeds on the ground and flies up into trees to rest and preen.

HABITAT: Overgrown fields, woodland edges and places with scattered tree. Habitat is more varied during migration.

DISTRIBUTION: Summer visitor to southern and central United States.

Lazuli Bunting

Passerina amoena

LENGTH: 5.5"

DESCRIPTION: An attractive bunting. Summer male is bright blue above from head to tail. Tip of the tail and wings are a little darker and wings have white bars. Breast and flanks are orange; the rest of the underside is white. Winter male loses some of the blue and is more brown-buff. Females are light brown above with a slight bluish wash in the wings and tail, a pale orange breast and off-white underparts. Juvenile similar to female but browner overall. Bill and legs gray in all forms.

VOICE: A loud *chik* and a jangled series of high notes including *whip-whip-whip-o-whip*.

BEHAVIOR: Often seen sitting atop bushes, on flowers and on wires, but is also happy feeding at ground level or on garden feeders.

HABITAT: Bushy areas and gardens.

DISTRIBUTION: Found throughout summer from Oklahoma north across the border to Canada and west right to the coast from California to Washington.

Painted Bunting
Passerina ciris

LENGTH: 5.5"

DESCRIPTION: Very brightly colored. Male has a blue head, vivid green-yellow back, wings and tail, bright red eye-ring, rump and underside and a slightly curved gray bill. Female is green above and pale yellow-buff below. Juvenile like a washed out female with a pale eye-ring. Legs dark and eyes black in all forms.

VOICE: A warbling sweet song consisting of many short notes.

BEHAVIOR: Forages on the ground and in bushes. Will visit feeders and brighten up the garden during winter.

HABITAT: Open scrub, bushy areas and gardens.

DISTRIBUTION: Two breeding populations are found in the United States, one from Texas to Missouri and the other from the east coast of Florida to North Carolina. A small number of birds winter in southern Florida but most travel further south to Central America.